The World's Greatest

Sherlock Holmes Quiz

DALE COPPS

Best Wishes,

Dale Copps

Sleuth Publications • San Francisco

TABLE OF CONTENTS

Sleuth Publications
689 Florida Street
San Francisco, CA 94110

ISBN   0-915341-25-5

Printed in the United States of America

INTRODUCTION

The Holmesian Phenomenon

Mr. Sherlock Holmes of Baker Street is a literary phenomenon. No other character in popular fiction has received such an overwhelming amount of attention. This attention has been of a very special sort. I doubt anyone can remember who began treating Holmes and Watson in this way, but whoever the imaginative pioneer was, thousands have followed in his footsteps.

That pioneer was a man who read Arthur Conan Doyle's tales of the great detective in the same wide-eyed way we ourselves read them when we first came across them as boys and girls. He followed Holmes's career from his startling meeting with Watson in the laboratory, to Watson's marriage which temporarily broke up their companionship, on through Holmes's supposed death—a death which, when first announced, sent hundreds into the streets of London wearing black armbands of mourning.

The tales were so alive with vivid recreations of Victorian England and so full of breathing humanity they began to transcend fiction. Our pioneer, an intelligent fellow no doubt, knew Sir Arthur had penned these tales which were appearing sporadically in the *Strand Magazine*, yet he chose to believe *Holmes really existed*, and with that choice, Holmesian scholarship came into being.

For it wasn't enough to believe Holmes existed. It now became necessary to know everything possible about him. Where did he actually live—the address he is credited with having doesn't exist. How old was he—the stories give only a rough idea. And what of all those discrepancies in the stories Watson wrote? (Of course Watson wrote them if Holmes actually existed.) Where was Watson's wound? How many times was he married? When did "The Adventure of Wisteria Lodge" really take place? These are all mysteries wrought by textual inconsistencies. And there are literally hundreds more.

Our pioneer soon had the assistance of thousands of otherwise sensible men and women, all happily believing in the true existence of Sherlock Holmes, and all willing to defend that belief and to seek the truth in an outpouring of books and articles concerning every tiny aspect of the great detective's life and of the lives of those around him.

This book is two books. First, it's a quiz to test your knowledge of all things Holmesian. Second, it's an introduction to the world of Holmesian (or Sherlockian) scholarship. Most of the questions and debates and complexities which have characterized Holmesian study over the past eighty years or so are here, and I offer my own humble explanations for some of them and leave others for you to ponder.

The Rules of the Game

The quiz part of this book is organized so that the easier sections are early in the book and the more difficult ones later. For this reason, it'll be good to do the sections in the order they are given. Another reason to do them this way is that what you learn about Holmes and Watson early on will be of use to you in later sections of the quiz.

The second quiz deals with titles of the stories. The answers are to be found immediately following in a complete list of all the stories. You may refer to that list in later quizzes, except where the individual instructions to the quizzes explicitly tell you not to.

You'll find a scorecard at the end of the quiz. Add up your score and determine whether you have won the G. Lestrade Booby Prize, the John H. Watson Meritorious If Unenlightened Companion Award, the Stanley Hopkins Promising Young Detective Commendation, or the Sherlock Holmes Grand Master Award of Awards.

I thank the following people who have assisted me in the writing of this book: Anne H. Gordon, for her great care in all stages of the book's production; Alfred Bester, for his many fine suggestions, among them the startling reminder of Professor Moriarty's place in the stories; Charles Goodman and Norman Nolan, two eminent Baker Street Irregulars whose assistance and support have been most helpful; and, of course, my parents, to whom this volume is dedicated.

FOR OPENERS

Get your hat.
You wish me to come?
Yes, if you have nothing better to do.

This first quiz is purely introductory. Twenty Questions, all "elementary," but nonetheless necessary before you can pass on to those airy heights of Sherlockian scholarship. One point each.

1. The name of the most famous detective in the world.

2. His all-but-constant companion.

3. His "long-suffering landlady."

4. His principal address during his active years.

5. His present address.

6. The number of his adventures which have been chronicled.

7. One of the two names which Sherlockians give to the collected chronicles.

8. The title given to Sir Arthur Conan Doyle by Sherlockians.

9. The name of the great detective's unofficial detecting organization.

10. The name of its first leader.

11-13. Name three of the four most prominent Scotland Yard detectives appearing in the chronicles.

14. The detective's chronicler is a veteran of which campaign?

15. He has an old wound. Where is it?

16. When did he meet the great detective?

17. Who introduced them?

18. What were the great detective's first ten words spoken directly to his new friend?

19. What was his friend's reply?

20. Name their first case together.

TITLES

John H. Watson, M.D., Late Indian Army

Dr. Watson was very careful of his own title and also took great care that the titles of his little pieces had just the proper touch of drama—though Holmes continually objected to his fondness for the sensational. Below are three sets of single words plucked from the story titles. They are, for the most part, the "drama" words in the titles. See how many of the blanks representing the other words in each title you can fill in. One point for each fully correct title.

NUMBERS:

____ ____ ____ ____ Solitary ____
____ ____ ____ ____ Second ____
____ ____ ____ ____ Three ____
____ ____ ____ ____ ____ Three-Quarter
____ ____ ____ Four
____ Five ____ ____
____ ____ ____ ____ Six ____
____ Last ____
____ Final ____

COLORS:

____ ____ ____ Black ____
____ ____ ____ ____ Red ____
____ Red-____ ____
____ ____ ____ Scarlet
____ ____ ____ ____ Golden ____ ____
Silver ____
____ Yellow ____

_____ _____ Orange _____
_____ _____ _____ _____ Blue _____
_____ _____ _____ _____ Copper _____

AND THINGS THAT GO BUMP IN THE NIGHT:

_____ _____ _____ _____ Creeping _____
_____ _____ _____ _____ Missing _____ - _____
_____ _____ _____ _____ Dying _____
_____ _____ _____ _____ Blanched _____
_____ _____ _____ _____ Empty _____
_____ _____ _____ _____ Veiled _____
_____ _____ Ritual
_____ _____ Puzzle
_____ _____ _____ Mystery
_____ _____ Problem

Points: 30

Your Score: _____

PARTNERS IN CRIME

Here's ... a full account of Ricoletti of the club-foot, and his abominable wife

Double trouble comes Holmes's way when he encounters the nefarious partnerships scrambled below. You are to match them up and place them in the proper stories. A point for the match; a point for the story.

1. Hugo Oberstein
2. Sir George Burnwell
3. Rachel Howells
4. Jonathan Small
5. Professor Coram
6. Von Bork
7. Count Negretto Sylvius
8. Leonardo the Strong Man
9. Alex
10. John Clay

A. Old Man Cunningham
B. Sam Merton
C. Baron Von Herling
D. Colonel Valentine Walter
E. Tonga
F. Archie
G. Mary Holder
H. Anna
I. Mrs. Ronder
J. Brunton

A.K.A.

It was bad English, but good American.

The Canon abounds in aliases. The gentlemen in the left-hand column below employed the aliases found in the right-hand column. Now match the number to the letter (the real name to the alias) and name the story in which they appear. One point for the match; one for the story.

1. Mr. Sherlock Holmes
2. "Killer" Evans
3. Birdie Edwards
4. Holy Peters
5. Mr. Windibank
6. Sutton
7. Sergius _____?_____
8. Don Muressington
9. Mr. Neville St. Clair
10. John Clay

A. Mr. Henderson
B. Altamont
C. Professor Coram
D. John Garrideb
E. Hosmer Angel
F. Vincent Spaulding
G. John Douglas
H. Rev. Dr. Shlessinger
I. Mr. Blessington
J. Hugh Boone

OUR MASTER'S VOICE I

Detection is, or ought to be, an exact science. . . .

Holmes is the master of cold logic. (Never mind that most of his "deductions" are actually inductions nor that his task of ferreting out the truth often required a sophisticated understanding of the human—and occasionally lower animal—heart.) Many were the dreary afternoons he and Watson would sit in their rooms in Baker Street, and Holmes would descant upon the rigors of his discipline. Below is a selection of his words, with the operative word or words missing. You are to supply them. One point for a direct hit; half a point for a synonym.

1. "I never _____. It is a shocking habit—destructive to the logical faculty."

2. "An exception _____ the rule."

3. "There is nothing so unnatural as the _____."

4. "It has long been an axiom of mine that the _____ things are infinitely the most important."

5. "It is a capital mistake to _____ in advance of the facts."

6. "Circumstantial evidence is occasionally very convincing, as when you find a _____ in the milk, to quote Thoreau's example."

7-8. "When you have eliminated the _____, whatever remains, however _____, must be the truth."

9. "When a fact appears to be opposed to a long train of deductions, it invariably proves to be capable of bearing some other _____."

10. "The grand thing is to be able to reason _____."

11. "There is nothing more deceptive than an _____ fact."

12. "I am a _____, Watson. The rest of me is a mere appendix."

13. "My mind rebels at _____. Give me problems, give me work...."

14-15. "I can discover _____, Watson, but I cannot _____ them."

16. "I should never _____, lest I bias my judgment."

17-18. "_____ is common. _____ is rare."

19. "One forms provisional theories and waits for time or fuller knowledge to _____ them."

20. "You know my _____. Apply them, and it will be instructive to compare results."

MEMORABLE VILLAINS

He is the worst man in London.

The Canon is full of nastiness, and among the nastiest are the folks identified below by nickname, *modus operandi*, or other endearing trait of character. It is gratifying to know that Holmes, whose career did include a few outstanding failures, saw most of these individuals off on their way to Hell. Name the person referred to and identify the principal story in which each takes part. One point for identification; one for story.

1. Who was "the worst man in London"?

2. Who was "The Napoleon of Crime"?

3. Who was "the second most dangerous man in London"?

4. Who was "the fourth smartest man in London"?

5. Who was "the Tiger of San Pedro"?

6. Who was "the daintiest thing under a bonnet on this planet"?

7. Who was the Andaman Island savage Holmes first suspected might be a species of lower primate?

8. Which vicious brute murdered one stepdaughter and almost killed another in a vain attempt at capturing their legacies?

9. What villain deluded another stepdaughter by impersonating a lover and then disappearing, hoping her broken heart and her money would thus stay in the family?

10. What sweet-talking Knight of the Realm induced a niece to lose her heart to him, and then her reputation in an aborted robbery scheme?

11. Name the ghastly assassin of the KKK who followed his prey across the Atlantic.

12. Name another secret-society paid assassin whose trip from America resulted in his own deserved death?

13. Name the jealous husband who wasn't satisfied with killing his wife and her lover, but mutilated them as well.

14. Who was the social climber who lived under an alias and decided the laws of succession needed a little help?

15. Which nasty student stole the test questions?

OPEN AND SHUT

*We have had some dramatic
entrances and exits
upon our small stage at Baker Street.*

The following is a two-part quiz consisting of ten first lines and ten last lines of some of the most famous stories. (Seventeen stories in all—three stories are represented by their first and last lines). Look for the internal clues—you'll find them in most of the examples. Name the stories for one point each.

FIRST LINES

1. "'I have some papers here,' said my friend Sherlock Holmes as we sat one winter's night on either side of the fire, 'which I really think, Watson, that it would be worth your while to glance over.'"

2. "It was nine o'clock at night upon the second of August—the most terrible August in the history of the world."

3. "It was in the year '95 that a combination of events, into which I need not enter, caused Mr. Sherlock Holmes and myself to spend some weeks in one of our great university towns, and it was during this time that the small but instructive adventure which I am about to relate befell us."

4. "In the year 1878 I took my degree of Doctor of Medicine of the University of London, and proceeded to Netley to go through the course prescribed for surgeons in the Army."

5. "During my long and intimate acquaintance with Mr. Sherlock Holmes I had never heard him refer

11

to his relations, and hardly ever to his own early life."

6. "Sherlock Holmes took his bottle from the corner of the mantelpiece, and his hypodermic from its neat morocco case."

7. "To Sherlock Holmes she is always *the* woman."

8. "It is with a heavy heart that I take up my pen to write these last words in which I shall ever record the singular gifts by which my friend Mr. Sherlock Holmes was distinguished."

9. "'I am inclined to think—' said I."

10. "I had called upon my friend, Mr. Sherlock Holmes, one day in the autumn of last year and found him in deep conversation with a very stout, florid-faced, elderly gentleman with fiery red hair."

AND NOW TEN LAST LINES...

1. "The famous air-gun of Von Herder will embellish the Scotland Yard Museum, and once again Mr. Sherlock Holmes is free to devote his life to examining those little problems which the complex life of London so plentifully presents."

2. "If you will have the goodness to touch the bell, Doctor, we will begin another investigation, in which also a bird will be the chief feature."

3. "'*Populus me sibilat, at mihi plaudo Ipse domi simul ac nummos contemplar in arca.*'"

4. "'When we have finished at the police-station, I think that something nutritious at Simpson's would not be out of place.'"

5. "'Watson,' said he, 'if it should ever strike you that I am getting a little over-confident in my powers, or giving less pains to a case than it deserves, kindly whisper "Norbury" in my ear, and I shall be infinitely obliged to you.'"

6. "'We also have our diplomatic secrets,' said he and, picking up his hat, he turned to the door."

7. "'Well, well, Inspector, I often ventured to chaff you gentlemen of the police force, but *Cyanea capillata* very nearly avenged Scotland Yard.'"

8. "Of their terrible chief, few details came out during the proceedings, and if I have now been compelled to make a clear statement of his career, it is due to those injudicious champions who have endeavoured to clear his memory by attacks upon him whom I shall ever regard as the best and wisest man whom I have ever known."

9. "We did at last hear that somewhere far out in the Atlantic a shattered stern-post of the boat was seen swinging in the trough of a wave, with the letters 'L. S.' carved upon it, and that is all which we shall ever know of the fate of the *Lone Star*."

10. "I have a check for five hundred pounds which should be cashed early, for the drawer is quite capable of stopping it if he can."

ON STAGE

You would have made an actor and a rare one

When Holmes sets out to be something other than a cool and methodical detective, he is able to rise to his roles with skill and daring. Answer the following questions for one point each.

1. Where does the quotation above come from?

2. In which story does Holmes impersonate *both* a drunken lout and a whimsical clergyman?

3. In which story is Holmes disguised as an elderly and somewhat deformed bibliophile?

4. Name either one of the two stories in which a goatee is part of his disguise.

5. In one story, Holmes convinces Mrs. Hudson and Watson he is suffering from a deadly fever. Name the story.

6. In which story does Holmes upset a dish of oranges and a carafe of water?

7. In which two stories does Holmes make use of a statue of himself center stage while he is off plotting in the wings?

8. Even Mycroft gets into the "act." In which story does he briefly appear as a coachman?

9. Late in the Canon, Watson is called upon to play his own roles. In which story does he impersonate a dealer in Oriental pottery, with an almost fatal lack of success?

10. Watson plays the somewhat less active role of a chauffeur more believably. Name the story.

DAINTY THINGS

*Women are never to be entirely trusted —
not the best of them*

Holmes had a famous lack of affection for women. It is nonetheless true that he always treated them a good deal better than he did any of the men he knew, including Watson. We must conclude from this that Holmes was prey to that general Victorian attitude toward women as weak, both mentally and physically, and in need of careful masculine treatment and protection. This attitude, of course, prevailed throughout most of this century as well, and is only now dying an agonizing death.

Holmes should have known better. At least twice he was soundly defeated by a woman, and in those rare instances when he called upon their aid, they conducted themselves with minimum fuss and maximum efficiency. Neither Watson nor Lestrade nor even Wiggins could claim as much.

Below are quotations and questions and sometimes just little hints pointing to the identity of a woman who figured in the Canon. One point for the identity; one for the story involved.

1. "Good-night, Mister Sherlock Holmes."

2. "Of course it has moved. Am I such a farcical bungler, Watson, that I should erect an obvious dummy, and expect that some of the sharpest men in Europe would be deceived by it."

3-4. "Name two of the four "Violets" who appear in the Canon and place them in their proper stories.

5. An emerald tie-pin.

6. "An arm—a woman's arm—shot from among the leaves. At the same instant the Baron uttered a horrible cry... 'Water! For God's sake, water!'"

7. "In my experience of women which extends over many nations and three separate continents I have never looked upon a face which gave a clearer promise of a refined and sensitive nature."

8. Who was the one woman who mourned for Selden?

9. A small blue bottle on the mantelpiece at Baker Street, containing prussic acid.

10. "Too late! Too late! I took the poison before I left my hiding place."

11. An even more ingenious suicide, with a gun and a length of twine.

12. The woman who never existed, though she was Lestrade's first suspect in an early case.

13. She flees after having immured her old lover alive in a tomblike structure.

14. This old lady was the "inside man" on the job and signalled Holmes when the coast was clear.

15. "Take that, you hound—and that!—and that!—and that!—and that!"

OUR MASTER'S VOICE II

Elementary, my dear Watson.

Here is another section of quotations of Sherlock Holmes. Most contain definite clues as to which story they appear in. Others, however, are really so well known that proper Sherlockians should know where they come from. One point for identifying each story.

1. "Elementary, my dear Watson."

2. "The features are given to man as the means by which he shall express his emotions, and yours are faithful servants."

3. "Indeed, I cannot think why the whole bed of the ocean is not one solid mass of oysters, so prolific the creatures seem."

4. "Is there any point to which you would wish to draw my attention?"
   "To the curious incident of the dog in the night-time."
   "The dog did nothing in the night-time."
   "That is the curious incident." (Only the italics are Holmes.)

5. ". . .it is best I should not leave the country. Scotland Yard feels lonely without me, and it causes an unhealthy excitement among the criminal classes."

6. "The world is big enough for us. No ghosts need apply."

7. "He is my hated rival upon the Surrey shore."

8. "Come, Watson, come!. . . The game is afoot. Not a word! Into your clothes and come!"

9. "You're not hurt Watson? For God's sake, say that you are not hurt!"

10. "I play the game for the game's own sake."

11. "Your life is not your own.... Keep your hands off it."

12. "He is the organizer of half that is evil and of nearly all that is undetected in the great city. He is a genius, a philosopher, an abstract thinker. He has a brain of the first order. He sits motionless, like a spider in the centre of its web, but that web has a thousand radiations, and he knows well every quiver of each of them."

13. "It is my belief, Watson, founded upon my experience that the lowest and vilest alleys in London do not present a more dreadful record of sin than does the smiling and beautiful countryside."

14. "Good old Watson! You are the one fixed point in a changing age. There's an East Wind coming all the same, such a wind as never blew on England yet. It will be cold and bitter, Watson, and a good many of us may wither before its blast. But it's God's own wind, none the less, and a cleaner, better, stronger land will lie in the sunshine when the storm has cleared."

15. "I might suggest that you have gone about in fear of some personal attack within the last twelve-month."

16. "I've found it! I've found it!... I have found a re-agent which is precipitated by haemoglobin, and by nothing else."

17. "It is cocaine...a seven per cent solution. Would you care to try it?"

18. "Well, sir, if it isn't too great a liberty, I am a neighbor of yours, for you'll find my little book-shop at the corner of Church Street, and very happy to see you, I am sure. Maybe you collect yourself, sir. Here's *British Birds*, and *Catullus*, and *The*

Holy Wars—a bargain, every one of them. With five volumes you would just fill that gap on that second shelf. It looks untidy, does it not, sir?"

19. "You can give me the glad hand to-night, mister... I'm bringing home the bacon at last."

20. "It was the towel which misled me. The poor fellow had never thought to dry himself, and so I in turn was led to believe that he had never been in the water. Why, then, should the attack of any water creature suggest itself to me?"

SUPERLATIVES

Why not tell them of the Cornish horror—
strangest case I have handled

Both Holmes and Watson are much given to superlatives. If we are to believe Watson, nearly every case which came along was "the most singular" in all Holmes's career. Below, however, are ten definite superlatives. Answer each for one point, and on this section you are *not* allowed to refer to the title list in the front portion of the book.

1. Chronologically, which is Holmes's first case?

2. Which is his last?

3. Of the following "long" stories, which is the longest?
   A Study in Scarlet
   The Sign of Four
   The Hound of the Baskervilles
   The Valley of Fear

4. Of the following short stories, which is the *longest*? (It is also the longest short story in the Canon.)
   "The Adventure of the Red Circle"
   "The Naval Treaty"
   "The Reigate Puzzle"
   "The Adventure of the Shoscombe Old Place"

5. Which of the following is the shortest story in the Canon?
   "The Adventure of the Veiled Lodger"
   "The Adventure of the Noble Bachelor"
   "The Final Problem"
   "The Adventure of the Missing Three-Quarter"

6. Which is the longest title in the Canon?

7. Which is the shortest?

8. Which is the highest story in the Canon?

9. Which is the lowest?

10. And finally, I must admit a somewhat subjective question: based upon the social position of the participants, which is the grandest story in the Canon?

MIDWAY

The plot thickens.

"For Openers" was the first general question-and-answer quiz. Now that we're about halfway along in the quiz section, here's "Midway"—20 questions a little tougher to answer than the first set. So on these, give yourself 2 points each for a correct answer. You may *not* refer to the list of titles in answering this section.

1-3. It may be failure to prevent a crime, to apprehend the criminal, or simply to comprehend the situation, but Holmes surely fails in at least six cases. Name three of them.

4-7. By my count, there are seven cases in the Canon entirely without a crime, though they do contain an occasional indiscretion of some weight and all at first *seem* to contain crime. Name four of them.

8-10. Three essential placements—where does Holmes keep his cigars, his tobacco, and his correspondence?

11. What does Watson own which used to belong to his brother?

12. Where did Holmes live before 221B Baker Street?

13. In what story are the Mormons a predominant factor?

14. How many steps are there leading up to Holmes's and Watson's rooms in Baker Street?

15. What was Irene Adler's formal occupation?

16. Name one of the three stories where a wedding ceremony figures in the plot.

17. What was Holmes's favorite weapon?

18. What is the name of Mycroft Holmes's club?

19. Where was the Borgia Pearl?

20. Name one of the three cases Holmes takes on and sees through without ever leaving his rooms in Baker Street.

NEWS BITS

Have you yesterday's Times, *Watson?*

The Canon is filled with newspapers. Sometimes the rooms at Baker Street seem strewn with them. Watson will read every part of them, we suspect starting with the sports pages to check on his bets, but Holmes only reads the "agony column," what we now call the "Personals." He advertises in the papers often when seeking to entrap a wanted man, and the news stories alternately provide laughter and shock to the detective when Watson turns up something of interest in a current case. Below are bits from the newspapers—stories and clippings from the agony column. Identify the story for one point each.

1. "A discovery has just been made by the Parisian police which raises the veil which hung round the tragic fate of Mr. Eduardo Lucas, who met his death by violence last Monday night at Godolphin Street...."

2   "The path is clearing. If I find chance signal message remember code agreed—one A, two B, and so on. You will hear soon. G."

3. "Found at the corner of Goodge Street, a goose and a black felt hat. Mr. Henry Baker can have the same by applying at 6:30 this evening at 221B, Baker Street."

4. ". . . Sir Charles' health has for some time been impaired and . . . Dr. James Mortimer, the friend and medical attendant of the deceased, has given evidence to the same effect."

5. "Wanted, woman of good address, attired like a lady. She has a remarkably thick nose, with eyes which are set close upon either side of it...."

6. "On account of the bequest of the late Ezekiah Hopkins, of Lebanon, Pennsylvania, U.S.A., there is now another vacancy open which entitles...."

7. **"A GRUESOME PACKET**
Miss Susan Cushing, living at Cross Street, Croydon, has been made the victim of what must be regarded as a peculiarly revolting practical joke..."

8. "A marriage has been arranged and will, if rumour is correct, very shortly take place between Lord Robert St. Simon, second son of the Duke of Balmoral, and Miss Hatty Doran, the only daughter of Aloysius Doran, Esq. of San Francisco, Cal., U.S.A."

9. **"CRIME IN THE CITY**
MURDER AT MAWSON & WILLIAMS
A desperate attempt at robbery, culminating in the death of one man and the capture of the criminal, occurred this afternoon in the City.... It appears that last week a new clerk named Hall Pycroft was engaged by the firm...."

10. "£10 reward. The number of the cab which dropped a fare at or about the door of the Foreign Office in Charles Street at quarter to ten in the evening of May 23d. Apply 221B, Baker Street."

UNI-CLUE

Norbury

The following single words should cause a flood of association to wash over you. Your task is simple: give the meaning or significance of the word for one point and the story in which it appears for another.

1. Baritsu.

2. Leprosy.

3. Phosphorus.

4. Lassus.

5. Pinkerton.

6. Submarine.

7. Bees.

8. £6,000.

9. Circus.

10. V.R.

ENTER TROUBLE

Now is the dramatic moment of fate, Watson,
when you hear a step upon the stair
which is walking into your life,
and you know not whether for good or ill.

The joys of Holmes's life were the miseries and mysteries brought to him by an endless stream of unhappy petitioners, from landladies to monarchs, from Scotland Yard to the underworld informers. Every entrance into Baker Street was made with the same goal in mind —relief from suffering—and yet all of them were different and not a few were absolutely sensational. Below are a selection of these entrances and/or early moments in the case; some tearful, some raging. Occasionally I have deleted a name which in itself would give the story away. Name the stories now from the information given about the nature of the case. One point each.

1. " 'Holmes,' said I as I stood one morning in our bow-window looking down the street, 'here is a madman coming along. It seems rather sad that his relatives should allow him to come out alone....'

   "A few moments later he was in our room, still puffing, still gesticulating, but with so fixed a look of grief and despair in his eyes that our smiles were turned in an instant to horror and pity. For a while he could not get his words out, but swayed his body and plucked at his hair like one who has been driven to the extreme limits of his reason. Then, suddenly springing to his feet, he beat his head against the wall with such force that we both rushed upon him and tore him away to the centre of the room."

2. "'My name is Dr. _____ _____ ,' said our visitor, 'and I live at 403 Brook Street.'

"'Are you not the author of a monograph upon acute nervous lesions?' I asked.

"'I so seldom hear of the work that I thought it was quite dead,' said he. 'My publishers gave me a most discouraging account of its sale. You are yourself, I presume, a medical man?'

"'A retired army surgeon.'

"'My own special hobby has always been nervous disease.'"

3. "'Ha! You put me off, do you?' said our visitor, taking a step forward and shaking his hunting-crop. 'I know you, you scoundrel! I have heard of you before. You are Holmes, the meddler.'

"My friend smiled.

"'Holmes, the busybody.'

"His smile broadened.

"'Holmes, the Scotland Yard Jack-in-office!'

"Holmes chuckled heartily. 'Your conversation is most entertaining,' said he. 'When you go out close the door, for there is a decided draught.'

"'I will go when I have had my say. Don't you dare to meddle with my affairs. I know that Miss _____ has been here. I traced her! I am a dangerous man to fall foul of! See here.' He stepped swiftly forward, seized the poker, and bent it into a curve with his huge brown hands."

4. "'What am I to do? That's what I ask you Mr. Holmes. There's Moorhouse, first reserve, but he is trained as a half, and he always edges right in on to the scrum instead of keeping out on the touchline. He's a fine place-kick, it's true, but then he has no judgment, and he can't sprint for nuts. Why, Morton or Johnson, the Oxford fliers, could romp round him . . . .'"

5.   (A HOLMES ENTRANCE)
     " He strode into the room, his hat upon his head
and a huge barbed-headed spear tucked like an
umbrella under his arm.
     "'Good gracious, Holmes!' I cried ....
     "He chuckled as he poured out the coffee.
     "'If you could have looked into Allardyce's back
shop, you would have seen a dead pig swung from
a hook in the ceiling, and gentleman in his shirt
sleeves furiously stabbing at it with this weapon. I
was that energetic person, and I have satisfied myself that by no exertion of my strength can I transfix
the pig with a single blow. Perhaps you would care
to try?'"

6.   "'It is easy to see that your experience has been no
common one, Mr. _____,' said he. 'Pray lie down
there and make yourself absolutely at home ....'
     "'Thank you,' said my patient, 'but I have felt
another man since the doctor bandaged me, and I
think that your breakfast has completed the cure. I
shall take up as little of your valuable time as
possible, so I shall start at once upon my peculiar
experiences.'"

7.   "A man entered who could hardly have been less
than six feet six inches in height, with the chest and
limb of a Hercules. His dress was rich with a rich-
ness which would, in England, be looked upon as
akin to bad taste ....
     "'You had my note?' he asked with a deep harsh
voice and a strongly marked German accent. 'I told
you I would call .... You may address me as the
Count Von Kramm.'"

8.   (Holmes is speaking to Watson) "For four years
I had seen nothing of him until one morning he
walked into my room in Montague Street ....
     "'How has all gone with you, _____?' I asked ....
     "'You probably heard of my poor father's death,'

said he; 'he was carrieed off about two years ago.
Since then I have of course had the Hurlstone estate
to manage, and as I am a member for my district as
well, my life has been a busy one. But I understand,
Holmes, that you are turning to practical ends
those powers which you used to amaze us?' "

9. " 'A most painful matter to me, as you can most
readily imagine, Mr. Holmes. I have been cut to the
quick. I understand that you have already managed
several delicate cases of this sort, sir, though I presume that they were hardly from the same class of
society.'
" 'No, I am descending.'
" 'I beg pardon.'
" 'My last client of the sort was a king.'
" 'What! Had he lost his wife?'
" 'You can understand. . .that I extend to the
affairs of my other clients the same secrecy which I
promise you in yours.' "

10. " 'This gentleman?' said he, with a wave in my
direction. 'Is it discreet? Is it right?'
" 'Dr. Watson is my friend and partner.'
" 'Very good, Mr. Holmes. It is only in your
client's interests that I protested. The matter is so
very delicate—'
" 'Dr. Watson has already heard of it.'
" 'Then we can proceed to business. You say that
you are acting for Lady Eva. Has she empowered
you to accept my terms?'
" 'What are your terms?'
" 'Seven thousand pounds.' "

11. " 'It was a clang of the bell, followed instantly by
heavy steps upon the stair. A moment later, our old
friend Lestrade appeared in the doorway. Over his
shoulder I caught a glimpse of one or two uni-
formed policemen outside.
" 'Mr. J____ H____ McF____?' said Lestrade.

"Our unfortunate client rose with a ghastly face.
" 'I arrest you for the wilful murder of Mr. J.
____ O____, of Lower ____.' "

12. (A lady speaks) " 'I have not yet described to you the most singular part. About six years ago—to be exact, upon the fourth of May, 1882—an advertisement appeared in the *Times* asking for the address of Miss ____ ____, and stating that it would be to her advantage to come forward.... I had at that time just entered the family of Mrs. Cecil Forrester in the capacity of governess. By her advice I published my address in the advertisement column. The same day there arrived through the post a small cardboard box addressed to me, which I found to contain a very large and lustrous pearl.' "

13. "As he entered his eyes fell upon the stick in Holmes's hand, and he ran towards it with an exclamation of joy. 'I am so very glad,' said he. 'I was not sure whether I had left it here or in the Shipping Office. I would not lose that stick for the world.'
" 'A presentation, I see,' said Holmes.
" 'Yes, sir.'
" 'From Charing Cross Hospital?' "

14. "We have had some dramatic entrances and exits upon our small stage at Baker Street, but I cannot recollect anything more sudden and startling than the first appearance of Thorneycraft Huxtable, M.A., Ph.D., etc.... [H]is first action, when the door had closed behind him, was to stagger against the table, whence he slipped down upon the floor, and there was that majestic figure prostrate and insensible upon our bearskin hearthrug."

15. (... And one exit)
" 'The law cannot, as you say, touch you,' said Holmes ... 'yet there never was a man who deserved

punishment more. If the young lady has a brother or friend, he ought to lay a whip across your shoulders. By Jove!' he continued, flushing up at the sight of the bitter sneer upon the man's face, 'it is not part of my duties to my client, but here's a hunting crop handy, and I think I shall just treat myself to—' He took two swift steps to the whip, but before he could grasp it there was a wild clatter of steps upon the stairs, the heavy hall door banged, and from the window we could see Mr. _____ _____ running at the top of his speed down the road."

CRYPTO-QUIZ

You look a little bewildered.

Holmes was an accomplished cryptologist. Among the veritable library of monographs to his credit is one analyzing 160 different codes. Unfortunately, we have the opportunity of experiencing those codes all too rarely in the stories themselves. Here is a small section devoted to some of Holmes's more visible work in cryptology. One point for each part of the two-part questions.

1. What is the significance of ETAOINSHRDL and in which story does this strange conglomeration of sounds occur?

2. Any proper Sherlockian will know the following code by heart. Insert the missing words for one point and name the story for the other:
   Whose was it?
   His who is _____.
   Who shall have it?
   He who will _____.
   Where was the _____?
   Over the oak.
   Where was the _____?
   Under the elm.
   (Really only half the message.)

3. In which stories are codes transmitted by:
   1) a flashing light
   2) a written and spoken foreign language.

4. Here is the first line of a written code. Name the story in which it appears and describe how it works:
   534 C2 13 127 36 31 4 7 21 41

33

5. READ THIS MESSAGE: The teacher, Miss Gloria, loves Walter Scott, and we had to write a paper in Communication class. She sent library books in to help this along the way.

PICK A MURDER

I have seen death in many forms.

The world of Sherlock Holmes—the gaslit avenues and drawing rooms of Victorian England—presents a general picture of civilized gentility, at least on the surface. But pierce that veneer of civilization and you encounter horror and inhumanity as awesome as any enormities practiced by the worst of Roman emperors or their barbaric adversaries. Below is a woundrous assortment of earthly departures—mostly murders, a suicide or two, here and there a justifiable homicide, and one case of just plain bad luck. A few of the killings were attempts which went astray, but most are unqualified successes. Name the recipient of each unnatural shuffling off of the old mortal coil for one point (using the list provided at the end of this question section) and the story involved for the other point.

1. Transfixed to the wall with a harpoon
2. Asphyxiation in a vault
3. Suicide by hanging
4. Burial alive in a split-level coffin
5. Shotgun blast in the face
6. Starvation and charcoal poisoning
7. Crushed to death by a hydraulic press
8. Killed by a poison dart
9. Death by gas
10. Death by multiple jellyfish stings

11. Death by combustible poison

12. Death by snakebite

13. Chewed to death

14. Shot to death with an air-gun

15. Kicked to death by a horse

(The list, by the way, doesn't pretend to exhaust the murders in the Canon, but merely to point out some of the most imaginative means.)

Now here's the list to match from:

Ronald Adair
Ted Baldwin
Sir Charles Baskerville
Brunton
Lady Frances Carfax
Peter Carey
Dr. Ray Ernest
Mr. Victor Hatherley
Paul Kratides
Fitzroy MacPherson
Arthur Pimmer
Bartholomew Sholto
Julie Stoner
Mr. Straker
Mortimer Tregennis

THE MASTER ACTS

How on Earth did you know that?

Here is a section central to any Holmes study—actual deductions by the Master leading to successful conclusions to tales. Most are crimes here, though I do give one instance of Holmes's amazing power of reading Watson's mind. Answer each question for one point and name the story from which it comes for another.

1. How does Holmes know Professor Coram is hiding someone in his bedroom?

2. How does he know Mr. Windibank and Hosmer Angel are the same man?

3. How does he conclude that Mrs. Gibson was a victim of suicide rather than a murder?

4. What famous clue first brought to Holmes's notice the dreadful business of the Abernetty family (an otherwise unchronicled case)?

5. How does Holmes conclude that the scene of Victor Hatherley's attack was very near the train station?

6. Why does Holmes conclude that Old Trevor had been "intimately associated with someone whose initials were J.A., and whom [he] afterwards [was] eager to entirely forget"?

7. How does Holmes conclude that Watson believes the American Civil War was a "preposterous way of settling a dispute"?

8. Give one of the three clues which led Holmes to name the student who stole the questions.

9. What was the bit of printed evidence which proved

"Killer" Evans was a fraud?

10. How was Holmes led to inferring the existence of a trapdoor in the floor of Eduardo Lucas's house?

ANIMAL KINGDOM

Re: Vampires

Holmes seems as unattracted to animals as to women, and though Watson mentions a bull-pup he owns when he meets Holmes, he apparently gets rid of it before they move in to 221B. However, there are animals aplenty in the Canon and their stories, and here are 20 questions relating to them. One point each.

  1-4. Name the *two* racehorses in the Canon and their stories.

  5-8. Name the two hounds Holmes uses for tracking and their stories.

  9-12. What are the two land-based killer animals in the Canon and in which stories do they appear?

13-14. Name the ocean killer and its story.

    15. Where was the blue carbuncle for a while?

    16. Who "sits motionless, like a spider in the centre of its web"?

    17. To what animal is Holmes compared in *A Study in Scarlet*, and quite often later in the Canon?

    18. On what did Holmes test the pills found in *A Study in Scarlet*?

    19. With what was the Creeping Man injected?

    20. How did the Veiled Lodger get that way?

QUOTABLES

I've heard that voice before ....

Here are 25 short quotations from the first 25 tales in the titles section—one per title—from *A Study in Scarlet* through "The Final Problem." A list of the speakers, in alphabetical order is provided at the end of the quotations. Be alert to the internal clues in the quotations, match the speaker with the statement, and name the story—for two points each.

1. "My indignation at this calm examination of our family documents overcame me ...."

2. "Effie loves me ... I know it .... But there's this secret between us ...."

3. "Your fate will be on your own head. *How long have you been here?*"

4. "My stepdaughter has been here! What has she been saying to you?"

5. "Whoever had lost a treasure, I knew that night I had gained one."

6. "Well ... you said you'd give me one for Christmas, and I was feeling which was the fattest."

7. "For seven hours I plied my trade, and ... found to my surprise that I had received no less than 26s. 4d."

8. "You crossed my path on the fourth of January. On the twenty-third you seriously incommoded me; by the middle of February ...."

9. "It is what we call a cataract knife."

10. "... there cannot be the least doubt ... that it has

been written by two people doing alternate words."

11. "I had to let myself go, and was hanging by my hands to the sill, when his blow fell."

12. "You mustn't blame me if you don't get on with him."

13. "Mother was all in favour from the first and was even fonder of him than I was."

14. "It was a long document, written in the French language containing twenty-six separate articles."

15. "Well, other people don't think quite so much of me as you seem to do, Mr. Pinner."

16. "He started me off upon the letter A, and then he left me."

17. "Who is this K.K.K. and why does he pursue this unhappy family?"

18. "Arthur!... you villain! you thief! How dare you touch that coronet?"

19. "My name, dear lad, is not _____ ."

20. "You took me in completely. Until after the alarm of fire, I had not a suspicion."

21. "My hair is somewhat luxuriant.... I could not dream of sacrificing it in this offhand fashion."

22. "Then you won't forgive me? You won't shake hands before I go?"

23. "I thought you had been dead this thirty years, Henry."

24. "I heard a cry of 'Cooee!' which was the usual signal between my father and myself."

25. "I was shocked to see that he was sitting bolt up-right in his chair, staring at me with a perfectly blank and rigid face."

Here are the speakers:

Irene Adler

Nancy Barclay

Victor Hatherley

Alexander Holder

Sherlock Holmes

Violet Hunter

James McCarthy

Mr. Melas

Professor Moriarty

Hattie Doran Moulton

Grant Munro

Reginald Musgrave

Percy Phelps

Hall Pycroft

Dr. Grimesby Roylott

James Ryder

Stamford

Neville St. Clair

Mr. Sutherland

Dr. Percy Trevelyan

Old Trevor

Dr. Watson (3 quotations)

Jabez Wilson

AN ELEMENTARY CHRONOLOGY

It was, then, in a year ... that shall be nameless.

It is a Herculean task, ultimately confronted, it seems, by most avid Sherlockians, to properly set all the tales into a real calendar. Watson was notoriously discreet about dates—which might, if carelessly revealed, have aided the curious in speculations concerning the identities he was so carefully masking. He was also notoriously sloppy at times (or was it the fault of that clumsy typesetter?). One story is said to take place during the period Holmes was out of England and was believed by all save Mycroft to be dead!

I shall not tax the minds of beginners and intermediate Sherlockians by requiring specific dates (except for one). Indeed, the dates of some stories are entirely a matter of inspired guesswork. But here is a two-part section concerning chronology, the first a series of questions for a point each, and the other a list of eight stories for you to put in their proper chronological order. One point for each story in its proper time "slot."

I.

1. What holiday is associated with "The Adventure of the Blue Carbuncle?"

2. Give the year of "The Adventure of the Empty House."

3. If you didn't know the time of year in "The Adventure of the Lion's Mane," why might you suspect it is summer?

4. Why is it unlikely "The Problem of Thor Bridge" took place in winter?

5-8. Give the hour, date, month, and year at the beginning of "His Last Bow."

II. Place in chronological order:

"The Final Problem"

"The Adventure of the Lion's Mane"

A Study in Scarlet

"The 'Gloria Scott'"

"The Boscombe Valley Mystery"

The Valley of Fear

"The Adventure of the Empty House"

"The Musgrave Ritual"

WEAPONS

Take that, you hound—and that!
—and that!—and that!—and that!

Weapons in the Canon are many and varied. Some are conventional (guns, knives) some more imaginative (the fangs of a snake and the hooves of a horse, for instance). Below are 15 weapons and 15 hapless individuals who met their deaths by them. Match them for one point each.

1. Handgun	A. Ronald Adair
2. Shotgun	B. Mrs. Amberley
3. Air gun	C. Ted Baldwin
4. Knife	D. Mr. Blessington (Sutton)
5. Sealing-wax knife	E. Captain James Calhoun
6. Rope	F. Mrs. Gibson
7. Club	G. Black Gorgiano
8. Rocks	H. Paul Kratides
9. Gas	I. Professor Moriarty
10. Water	J. Mr. Ronder
11. Poison dart	K. Victor Savage
12. Fangs	L. Selden
13. Devil's Foot	M. Bartholomew Sholto
14. Virus	N. Willoughby Smith
15. Charcoal fumes	O. Brenda Tregennis

FOREIGN SHORES

... many nations and three separate continents ...

Someday an eager Holmesian (perhaps yourself) will do a thorough analysis of the uses of foreigners and foreign nations in the Canon. The stories are full of them. Often, and this is particularly true in the earlier tales, foreign influence is responsible for much of the nastier dealings. London was more the center of the world in 1895 than it is today, and this could account for the flow of foreign traffic to her shores.

The statements below describe central issues in 15 of the stories, all concerned with foreign influence. Identify by name the person indicated by the word(s) in italics (using the checklist at the end of the section if you wish) for one point, and the story for another.

1. *She* brought her black child to England and kept her hidden.

2. On route to criminal exile in Australia, *his* ship blew up following a mutiny.

3. *He* followed his prey to England from the great alkali plain of Utah.

4. Holmes said the American born *Lady St. Simon* was a myth and never existed.

5. The Canon prefigures the Roaring Twenties in this tale of a *gangster* from Chicago.

6. *She* was Brazilian while her husband was American, and Holmes attributed her passionate jealousy to the torrid climate from which she came.

7. It is often surmised that this *mounted monarch* was really a veiled depiction of Prince Edward (later

King Edward VII), another fun-loving philanderer who had his problems with troublemaking women.

8. Another fiery Latin type, this time a deposed South American *despot*, outwits Holmes, but is eventually assassinated in a hotel in Madrid.

9. From Southern U.S.A., the unfortunate Openshaw family is pursued by *him* and his fellows, and eventually all are slain.

10. Yet another secret society in America, this time represented by an *Italian from New York*, comes seeking revenge in England.

11. When *he* shouted his old Autralian signal cry, his old Australian friend came by—and killed him.

12. At least two name changes didn't save *this man* from eventual death, though it took Moriarty's forces to do him in when the American pursuers failed.

13. Both *he* and his estranged wife were Russian exiles.

14. The *killer* brought his savage playmate with him from distant Agra, India.

15. The only story besides "The Final Problem" in which we witness Holmes in action outside of the British Isles. (Both points for this single answer.)

Here are the individuals you must identify:

Black Gorgiano

Captain James Calhoun

Professor Coram

John Douglas

Mrs. Gibson

Jefferson Hope

King of Bohemia

Charles McCarthy

Hattie Doran Moulton

Effie Munro

Don Murillo

Abe Slaney

Jonathan Small

Old Trevor

THE HOME STRETCH

Pray give my greetings to Mrs. Watson ...

Here are 20 questions in the general category begun with "For Openers" and continued in "Midway." Two points each.

1. How many stories does Mycroft Holmes actually appear in?

2-3. Name two of them.

4. How many stories does Professor Moriarty actually appear in?

5-6. Name the two stories written by Holmes.

7-8. Name the two stories written by an anonymous third person (not including the flashback sequences in *A Study in Scarlet* and *The Valley of Fear*).

9. What do the following people have in common: James McCarthy of "The Boscombe Valley Mystery"; Arthur Holder of "The Adventure of the Beryl Coronet"; Miss Dunbar of "The Problem of Thor Bridge"; and John Hector MacFarlane of "The Adventure of the Norwood Builder"?

10. What do these men have in common: James Phillimore, Archie Stamford, Colonel Warburton, and Bert Stevens?

11. Holmes shows knowledge of five languages in the Canon. Which are they? (It is not clear whether he is fluent in them all.)

12-13. Name two of the three cases where Holmes commits burglary. (Burglary: the act of breaking into any building at any time to commit theft or other felony.)

14. "All London was interested and the fashionable world dismayed" by what?

15. Where is the travel-worn and battered tin dispatch box of Watson's?

16. What title did Holmes give himself in *The Sign of Four*?

17. What was Holmes's level and regularity of cocaine consumption prior to *The Sign of Four*?

18. What do these men have in common: John Turner of "The Boscombe Valley Mystery"; James Ryder of "The Adventure of the Blue Carbuncle"; James Wilder of "The Adventure of the Priory School"; and Captain Crocker of "The Adventure of the Abbey Grange"?

19. A portion of which story takes place in an opium den?

20. What single affliction was Holmes reported to suffer occasionally as age crept upon him on the South Downs?

A RELATIONSHIP

It was worth a wound

Like Don Quixote and Sancho Panza, Holmes and Watson are inseparable in our imaginations—the one daring, certain, and inspired; the other a trifle dense, a bit clumsy, and always three steps behind, but none-theless ready to lay down his life for his friend. Here are ten questions for one point each which analyze this enduring relationship between two men so different, whose shared chemistry created the formula for their immortality.

1. What was "worth a wound"?

2-3. How many years was Holmes in active practice and for how many of those years did Watson co-operate with Holmes and chronicle his adventures?

4. In which case is Watson directly and unquestion-ably responsible for saving Holmes's life (as well as his own)?

5. At the *beginning* of how many of the 60 stories is Watson living with Holmes?

6. How did Holmes manage to get Watson to move back to Baker Street after the detective's return from his long disappearance?

7. What crime did Holmes threaten to commit for Watson's sake in "The Adventure of the Three Garridebs"?

8. What do these men have in common: Jackson, Verner, and Anstruther?

9. When did Holmes, for reasons of his client's nobility and the delicacy of the problem, ask Watson to leave the consultation?

10. What is our last view of Holmes and Watson?

SUPER-IMPOSSIBLES

You have an extraordinary genius for minutiae.

Here are 20 questions that would make all but the staunchest Holmesian weep with frustration in trying to answer. All the questions are pertinent to Holmes scholarship, however, and many are cause for a good deal of debate among the experts. I offer you a whopping three points each for correct answers.

1. How much did Holmes pay for his Stradivarius, where did he buy it, and from whom?

2. Who knocked out Holmes's left canine and where did it happen?

3. Name all six countries Holmes mentioned visiting during his disappearance (The Great Hiatus—1891-94).

4. What startling discovery had Holmes made just prior to meeting Watson for the first time?

5. What do these two men have in common: Sherman the bird-stuffer and Jeremy Dixon, Trinity College?

6. In which two stories does Holmes set "bogus" fires to gain ends?

7. Professor James Moriarty had a brother who defended him after his death. Name him.

8. Who was the Norwegian explorer Sigerson, and when was he heard from?

9. What does C.C.H. stand for?

10. What is the Ancient Order of Freemen?

11. When did Holmes have cause to quote from Eckermann's *Voodooism and the Negroid Religions*?

12. What was the "buried treasure" in Nathan Garrideb's room?

13. In whose future did Holmes have high hopes, and in what story does he first appear?

14. What do these men have in common: Morse Hudson, Dr. Barnicot, Mr. Horace Harker, Mr. Josiah Brown, and Mr. Sandeford?

15. In what case are a bell-pull and three wine glasses sufficient evidence to set Holmes upon the truth?

16. What do these men have in common: Sam Merton, Steve Dixie, and Grimesby Roylott?

17. Who is Billy?

18. In what story does Holmes speak of his "Agency"?

19. What mechanical device do these three stories have in common: "The Adventure of the Illustrious Client," "The Adventure of the Three Garridebs," and "The Adventure of the Retired Colourman"?

20. In which story do Holmes and Watson call each other by their first names?

ROGUES' GALLERY

The main portion of the quiz is now over. Coming up is an assortment of original English and American illustrations to the stories. Each one is accompanied by five questions concerning the pictures or the stories from which they come.

1.

1. Name the story.

2. Name the man in the house:
    a. Lysander Stark
    b. Jim Browner
    c. Col. Valentine Walter
    d. Black Gorgiano

3. Name the fellow outside.

4. How long of a drop is he about to have?

5. How does Elise figure in the story?

2.

1. Name the (very famous) story.

2. Who is the little man holding the flame?

3. What does he think the word on the wall means, and what does it really mean?

4. What is the address?

5. What is the most unique thing that happens to Holmes and Watson in the story—something which never happens to either of them again?

3.

1. What is the title of this story? (One of the characters here provides a hint.)

2. What "pet" does the man in the picture own?

3. What is the name of one of the women in the picture:
   a. Effie Munro
   b. Susan Cushing
   c. Nancy Devoe Barclay
   d. Hattie Doran Moulton

4. Who dies in this story?

5. What is the cause of death?

4.

1. Who is this elegant fellow?

2. Approximately how tall is he?

3. What significance does the name Count Von Kramm have in the story?

4. Holmes's fee is mentioned for the first time in this story. What is the "advance" from this fellow?

5. Name the story.

5.

1. What is the job of the young lady in this illustration?

2. What has happened to her physically which she has not welcomed?

3. What color is her dress?

4. What happens to her employer toward the end of the story?

5. Name the story.

6.

1. Name the story.

2. Name the two characters in the picture.

3. Of what significance in the story are the following items: Pope's *Homer*, two candlesticks, an ivory paperweight, an oak barometer, and a ball of twine?

4. Who dies in the story:
   a. Leonardo the strong man
   b. Billy the page
   c. Edward VII
   d. William the coachman

5. Whodunit?

7.

1. Name this story.

2. Who gets shot in the story:
   a. Carruthers
   b. Woodley
   c. Morton
   d. Miss Smith?

3. What has just been going on previous to the action in the illustration?

4. Why is the unfortunate woman in the picture so beset by conniving men?

5. Watson is granted a real privelege for the first time (in the order of the stories' publication) in this one. What is it?

8.

1. Where are Holmes and Watson?

2. What is Holmes hoping to find?

3. How did he know where to look?

4. What happened to the owner of the house they are in?

3. Who is the woman most intimately involved in this affair:
   a. Mrs. Trelawney Hope
   b. Irene Adler
   c. Lady Frances Carfax
   d. Martha

9.

1. What has just happened in this scene?

2. Identify any two of the three participants.

3. Name the story.

4. Who dies in the story?

5. Why does Sherlock Holmes describe the wife in this picture as a "myth"?

10.

1. Name the story.

2. What position did the man down the hole (now, alas, quite dead) occupy in the house?

3. Who killed him, and what happened to the killer?

4. What help does Watson give to Holmes in this story?

5. Jewels are found in this story which belong to an old English line of royalty. Name the family.

11.

1. Name this man.

2. How does Isa Whitney figure into this story?

3. Where does Watson run into Holmes in the story, much to his surprise?

4. Who is Boone, and how does he figure into the story?

5. By what name is Watson called in this story—a name no one ever calls him again?

12.

1. Name the killer.

2. To whom will he shortly send a package?

3. Why does he send it to this person?

4. Name two of Watson's paintings mentioned in this story.

5. Who is the mystery writer Holmes mentions in this story?

13.

1. Name the story.

2. What is beeswing?

3. What is the famous Holmes quotation which appears in this story?

4. Whodunit?
   a. Captain Crocker
   b. Captain Calhoun
   c. Colonel Moran
   d. Sir Eustace Brackenstall

5. What is the maid's name?
   a. Eugenie
   b. Martha
   c. Theresa
   d. Violet

14.

1. What story is depicted in this, perhaps the most famous original illustration in the Canon?

2. Name the setting.

3. Name the year the action takes place.

4. Where is Watson at this moment?

5. Who, besides the two fighters here depicted, is also in the vicinity?

ANSWERS to FOR OPENERS

1. Mr. Sherlock Holmes. (No middle name is ever mentioned.)
2. John H. Watson, M.D.
3. Mrs. Hudson.
4. 221B Baker Street, London W1, England.
5. In a small farm upon the Sussex Downs about five miles from Eastbourne, with a view of the English Channel and the White Cliffs of Dover.
6. Sixty—four long and fifty-six short stories. As it happens, there is one for each year of his chronicled life, from his university days to "His Last Bow," at the dawn of the Great War. (Keep that in mind—it's sure to turn up again.)
7. The Canon or Sacred Writings.
8. The Literary Agent. Some Sherlockians believe he overstepped his bounds as Watson's agent and wrote some of the stories himself. Others have been known to say he wrote them all. I cannot recall any suggestion to the effect that he *was* Watson, though I myself find the notion conceivable, if somewhat unwieldy.
9. The Baker Street Irregulars. Now immortalized in a great American organization.
10. Wiggins.
11-13. G. Lestrade, Tobias Gregson, Stanley Hopkins, and Athelney Jones.
14. Afghanistan.
15. Who knows for sure? It is one of the most enduring mysteries in the Canon. Watson talks of both a shoulder wound and a leg wound, but only in the singular—as his *wound*, not *wounds*. One does not have to imagine a grotesque posture for the good doctor (bent over a patient on the battlefield?) nor an unusually difficult angle fo fire (from horseback?) to visualize one gunshot

creating both wounds. A single bullet and a single moment of being wounded might be cause enough for Watson to refer simply to his *wound*, and he might ascribe it to either shoulder or leg, depending upon which of the two areas was acting up at the time.

16. Another point of great controversy. Almost surely in January—very possibly on the first of the month—as the Baker Street Irregulars believe, but was it in 1881 or 1882? Rather than go through the mass of evidence for each, take credit if you guessed either.

17. Young Stamford, a former colleague of Watson's in St. Bartholomew's Hospital. They met in the Criterion Bar.

18. "How are you? You have been in Afghanistan, I perceive." Words that will live forever.

19. "How on earth did you know that?" (As the old vaudevillean might have said, "Watson, you ain't seen nothin' yet!")

20. *A Study in Scarlet.*

Points: 20

Your Score: _____

ANSWERS to TITLES

Your Majesty had not spoken before I was aware that I was addressing Wilhelm Gottsreich Sigismond von Ormstein, Grand Duke of Cassel-Felstein, and hereditary King of Bohemia.

Only Holmes could be expected to remember all those titles of a fairly obscure monarch. You won't be expected to. What follows here is not a quiz, but rather a list of all the titles of the stories (novels included) which are in the Canon. The list is in the order they were originally published in book form. Except for the preceding section and a few coming up, you may freely refer to this list to jostle your memory. I will point out in the introductions to the individual quizzes those which you should do without referring to this list.

A Study in Scarlet

The Sign of Four

THE ADVENTURES OF SHERLOCK HOLMES:

"A Scandal in Bohemia"
"The Red-headed League"
"A Case of Identity"
"The Boscombe Valley Mystery"
"The Five Orange Pips"
"The Man with the Twisted Lip"
"The Adventure of the Blue Carbuncle"
"The Adventure of the Speckled Band"
"The Adventure of the Engineer's Thumb"
"The Adventure of the Noble Bachelor"
"The Adventure of the Beryl Coronet"
"The Adventure of the Copper Beeches"

THE MEMOIRS OF SHERLOCK HOLMES:

"Silver Blaze"
"The Yellow Face"
"The Stock-broker's Clerk"
"The 'Gloria Scott'"
"The Musgrave Ritual"
"The Reigate Puzzle"
"The Crooked Man"
"The Resident Patient"
"The Greek Interpreter"
"The Naval Treaty"
"The Final Problem"

THE RETURN OF SHERLOCK HOLMES:

"The Adventure of the Empty House"
"The Adventure of the Norwood Builder"
"The Adventure of the Dancing Men"
"The Adventure of the Solitary Cyclist"
"The Adventure of the Priory School"
"The Adventure of Black Peter"
"The Adventure of Charles Augustus Milverton"
"The Adventure of the Six Napoleons"
"The Adventure of the Three Students"
"The Adventure of the Golden Pince-Nez"
"The Adventure of the Missing Three-Quarter"
"The Adventure of the Abbey Grange"
"The Adventure of the Second Stain"

The Hound of the Baskervilles

The Valley of Fear

HIS LAST BOW:

"The Adventure of Wisteria Lodge"
"The Adventure of the Cardboard Box"
"The Adventure of the Red Circle"
"The Adventure of the Bruce-Partington Plans"
"The Adventure of the Dying Detective"
"The Disappearance of Lady Frances Carfax"
"The Adventure of the Devil's Foot"
"His Last Bow"

THE CASEBOOK OF SHERLOCK HOLMES:

"The Adventure of the Illustrious Client"
"The Adventure of the Blanched Soldier"
"The Adventure of the Mazarin Stone"
"The Adventure of the Three Gables"
"The Adventure of the Sussex Vampire"
"The Adventure of the Three Garridebs"
"The Problem of Thor Bridge"
"The Adventure of the Creeping Man"
"The Adventure of the Lion's Mane"
"The Adventure of the Veiled Lodger"

"The Adventure of the Shoscombe Old Place"
"The Adventure of the Retired Colourman"

ANSWERS to PARTNERS IN CRIME

1(D). "The Adventure of the Bruce Partington Plans."
2(G). The Adventure of the Beryl Coronet." Young love.
3(J). "The Musgrave Ritual."
4(E). *The Sign of Four*. With the possible exception of Roylott and his snake, this is the most macabre partnership in the Canon.
5(H). "The Adventure of the Golden Pince-Nez." Forgive me if I keep coming back to this one—I think it one of the very best.
6(C). "His Last Bow." Ditto.
7(B). "The Adventure of the Mazarin Stone."
8(I). "The Adventure of the Veiled Lodger." Do you notice how the later stories are so much more gruesome than the earlier? Nothing from *The Adventures* can match "The Cardboard Box" from *His Last Bow* or this one from *The Casebook*.
9(A). "The Reigate Puzzle." It ran in the family.
10(F). "The Red-headed League."

Points: 20

Your Score: _____

ANSWERS to A.K.A.

1(B). "His Last Bow."
2(D). "The Adventure of the Three Garridebs," of

course. The quotation for this section comes from that story which Watson found so amusing, his own brush with death apparently notwithstanding.

3(G). *The Valley of Fear.*

4(H). "The Disappearance of Lady Frances Carfax." This one should have been a give-away to the trained observer.

5(E). "A Case of Identity." One of the nastier fellows to get off "scot-free," though Holmes did try to take a horsewhip to him.

6.(I). "The Resident Patient."

7(C). "The Adventure of the Golden Pince-Nez." Lung cancer, we suspect, finally claimed this other man the law could not touch.

8(A). "The Adventure of Wisteria Lodge." How a "Murillo" ever got away with a name like "Henderson" remains one of the wonderful enigmas of the Canon.

9(J). "The Man with the Twisted Lip."

10(F). "The Red-headed League."

Points: 20

Your Score: _____

ANSWERS to OUR MASTER'S VOICE I

1. "guess" (From *The Sign of Four*). Not precisely true. See "The Yellow Face," among others.
2. "disproves" (*The Sign of Four*)
3. "commonplace" ("A Case of Identity")
4. "little" ("A Case of Identity")
5. "theorize" ("The Second Stain"). But let him get hold of a fact and watch out: "The ideal reasoner would, when he had once been shown a single fact in all its bearings, deduce from it not only all the chain of events which led up to it, but also all the

results which would follow from it[!]" From "The Five Orange Pips."

6. "trout" ("The Noble Bachelor")

7-8. "impossible";"improbable" (*The Sign of Four*). *Deduct* one point if you missed these, the most famous of all Holmes's words on the science of deduction.

9. "interpretation" (*A Study in Scarlet*)

10. "backward" (*A Study in Scarlet*). "Together" is *not* acceptable.

11. "obvious" ("Boscombe Valley")

12. "brain" ("Mazarin Stone"). He was, after all, "the most perfect reasoning and observing machine that the world has seen," according to Watson.

13. "stagnation" (*The Sign of Four*)

14-15. "facts"; "change" ("Thor Bridge") Uncommonly humble, and again less than the truth—his influence upon the facts of justice spared many a criminal from the dock.

16. "marry" (*The Sign of Four*). I choose not to recall that eminent Holmesian who, in momentary delusion, posited a marriage for Holmes with Irene Adler, the issue being that excellent American Mr. Nero Wolfe. It's all too awful to imagine!

17-18. "Crime"; "Logic" ("The Copper Beeches")

19. "explode" ("The Sussex Vampire")

20. "methods" (*The Sign of Four*). Poor Watson, constantly being goaded on by Holmes to exercize all the intellect he just didn't have.

Points: 20

Your Score: _____

1. Charles Augustus Milverton, in the adventure of the same name.
2. Professor James Moriarty, a name to frighten naughty children with, and probably the third most famous name in the Canon. (Principally found in "The Final Problem," of course, but I'll give a half a point to any bewildered individual who comes up with *The Valley of Fear.*)
3. Colonel Sebastian Moran, Moriarty's chief lieutenant, and a crack shot ("The Adventure of the Empty House").
4. John Clay ("The Red-headed League"). But who were the first three? Mr. Martin Dakin, in his estimable book, *A Sherlock Holmes Commentary* says Professor Moriarty and Col. Moran have to be placed first and second respectively, and then posits a half dozen others, including Milverton. Here I think he has gone astray in underestimating Holmes's healthy ego. The great detective almost certainly placed himself (with reason, admittedly) at the top of the list, with Moriarty and Moran following.
5. Don Murillo, the ex-President of a banana republic ("The Adventure of the Wisteria Lodge").
6. Irene Adler ("A Scandal in Bohemia"). Holmes's first (male chauvinist) impression gave way to grudging admiration finally for this dainty thing, after she made a thorough fool of him *and* the King of Bohemia.
7. Tonga (*The Sign of Four*).
8. Dr. Grimesby Roylott ("The Adventure of the Speckled Band"). Surely one of the most perfect names for a villain in the whole Canon.
9. Mr. Windibank. ("A Case of Identity"). And he's all the more villainous for being beyond the law.
10. Sir George Burnwell ("The Adventure of the Beryl Coronet").
11. Captain James Calhoun ("The Five Orange Pips") Lost at sea, poor devil.

12. Black Gorgiano ("The Adventure of the Red Circle"). The closest thing to the modern Mafia in the Canon (see also "The Adventure of the Six Napoleons"), but this is one Godfather whose reach exceeded his grasp.
13. Jim Browner ("The Adventure of the Cardboard Box").
14. Jack Stapleton, the Baskerville incognito (*The Hound of the Baskervilles*).
15. Mr. Gilchrist ("The Adventure of the Three Students"). We believe he reformed and escaped the final hellish company of the preceding grand villains of the Canon.

Points: 30

Your Score: _____

ANSWERS to OPEN AND SHUT

FIRST LINES

1. "The 'Gloria Scott'" It's Watson's first look at Holmes's early work in the years before they met.
2. "His Last Bow." The awful and wonderful climax of Holmes's career.
3. "The Adventure of the Three Students." One can only speculate on Watson's reticence concerning the purpose of their journey.
4. *A Study in Scarlet.* The good Doctor's first words to his soon-to-be-adoring public.
5. "The Greek Interpreter." Enter Holmes's brother, the only man to whom he ever compared himself unfavorably, in the intellectual powers of observation.
6. *The Sign of Four.* Nasty habit, cocaine. It is believed Watson finally cured him of it.
7. "A Scandal in Bohemia." So why do we never hear

him mention her by name again?

8. "The Final Problem." Sad, but thankfully untrue.
9. *The Valley of Fear*. There is no real hint here, but the opening is so famous that you really ought to know it. Holmes's snippiness (is there a better word?) is soon put down by Watson in a very neat exchange.
10. "The Red-headed League." There—that heavy-handed hint made up for #9.

LAST LINES

1. "The Adventure of the Empty House."
2. "The Adventure of the Blue Carbuncle."
3. A *Study in Scarlet*. Watson's consolation to Holmes when Scotland Yard takes all the credit: The people may hiss me, but I applaud myself when the money starts rolling in. (Very freely translated.)
4. "The Adventure of the Dying Detective." For once after a case, Holmes doesn't run off to a concert. Understandably—he hasn't eaten in three days.
5. "The Yellow Face." It is not recorded that Watson ever took Holmes's advice. He did have opportunity enough.
6. "The Adventure of the Second Stain." The neatest put-down of a Prime Minister on written record.
7. "The Adventure of the Lion's Mane."
8. "The Final Problem." Ah, Watson, you have such a fine big heart! How could Holmes ever snap at you "cut out the poetry?" (see "The Retired Colourman.")
9. "The Five Orange Pips."
10. "His Last Bow." Chronologically, Holmes's last recorded words to Dr. Watson.

Points: 20

Your Score: _____

ANSWERS to ON STAGE

1. *The Sign of Four.* Athelney Jones of Scotland Yard says it, just after being shocked at Holmes's transformation before his eyes from an infirm old man back to himself.
2. "A Scandal in Bohemia." Neither did any good. She was just too clever for him.
3. "The Adventure of the Empty House." Holmes's insensitive homecoming.
4. "The Adventure of Charles Augustus Milverton" and "His Last Bow."
5. "The Adventure of the Dying Detective." To give Watson his due, he was forced to keep his distance from Holmes; otherwise, we hope, he would have caught on.
6. "The Reigate Puzzle."
7. "The Adventure of the Empty House" and "The Adventure of the Mazarin Stone." You must have both for your one point.
8. "The Final Problem." I've always found this rigorous action of Mycroft's inconceivable, knowing the sedentary habits of the man.
9. "The Adventure of the Illustrious Client."
10. "His Last Bow."

Points: 10

Your Score: _____

ANSWERS to DAINTY THINGS

1. Irene Adler's parting shot, delivered in disguise to Holmes outside his Baker Street door. It's her little way of telling him she was onto his scheme. ("A Scandal in Bohemia")
2. Holmes here is speaking of Mrs. Hudson who is

crawling around his apartment, presumably on all fours, moving the dummy and trying to avoid being a target for the nasties in "The Adventure of the Empty House."

3-4. Miss Violet Hunter ("The Adventure of the Copper Beeches"); Miss Violet Smith ("The Adventure of the Solitary Cyclist"); Miss Violet Westbury ("The Adventure of the Bruce-Partington Plans"); and Miss Violet de Merville ("The Adventure of the Illustrious Client")

5. A present from a "certain gracious lady," almost certainly the Queen herself, for Holmes's work in "The Adventure of the Bruce-Partington Plans."

6. The awful scene of the vitriol throwing from "The Adventure of the Illustrious Client." The woman with the golden arm: Miss Kitty Winter.

7. Watson's properly British description of love at first sight. Miss Mary Morstan is the recipient of his adulation here, in *The Sign of Four*, and will later receive his hand as well, in marriage. An ongoing controversy in the Canon centers around the number of times Watson marries. He certainly marries Mary in 1889 or perhaps 1888. She possibly dies around 1893 or 1894, and in subsequent confusing chronology of later tales, sometimes Watson is married and sometimes he is not. Anywhere from one to five wives have been ascribed to him. The other wives—if there were others have never been satisfactorily identified. Mary is the only certain wife of Watson, and when he and Holmes talk of Watson's recent "bereavement," ("The Adventure of the Empty House") neither specifically refers to the death of Mary. Is it conceivable she didn't die? Was there some other unrelated bereavement? Or might Mary have contracted some awful form of brain fever, perhaps while nursing one of Watson's patients, which left her mind in such a delicate condition she had, periodically, to be institutionalized? During these times, Watson may have moved back to Baker

Street, and whenever possible rejoined his wife in her healthier periods.

8. Selden, the criminal, was the man killed on the moor by *The Hound of the Baskervilles*. Watson said, "Evil indeed is the man who has not one woman to mourn him." Selden did; it was his sister, Mrs. Barrymore, a servant at Baskerville Hall.

9. The poison was sent to Holmes by Mrs. Eugenia Ronder in "The Adventure of the Veiled Lodger." The despairing woman would have killed herself with it had Holmes not shown her the value of her life. She sent it to him as her thanks and her guarantee.

10. Anna, in "The Adventure of the Golden Pince-Nez" was a successful suicide.

11. Mrs. Neil Gibson of "The Problem of Thor Bridge." "Hell hath no fury..."

12. As Holmes said "'Rache,' is the German word for 'revenge'; so don't lose your time looking for Miss Rachel." *A Study in Scarlet.*

13. Rachel Howells, in "The Musgrave Ritual."

14. Martha, in "His Last Bow." Speculation to the effect she was Mrs. Hudson is one of the more risible enormities of Sherlockian scholarship.

15. An unnamed great lady, in "The Adventure of Charles Augustus Milverton." The late nineteeth century was the golden age of the melodrama, and nothing is more wonderfully melodramatic than this forthright dispatching of the foul fiend. Also, this is another example of a woman getting away with her crimes. Holmes, who witnessed the murder, chalked it all up to a worthy effort at London sanitation.

Points: 30

Your Score: _____

1. In no story does Holmes ever say this line—a line which he is universally famous for having said. He *does* say simply, "Elementary," in "The Crooked Man"; he says "It was very superficial, my dear Watson, I assure you," in "The Resident Patient"; and again he says exactly the same thing in "The Cardboard Box." There are doubtless other examples of near-misses to "Elementary, my dear Watson," and I invite you to find them, but don't waste your time looking for that one phrase everybody *knows* Sherlock Holmes said.

2. "The Adventure of the Cardboard Box." I've always enjoyed Holmes's delicately sarcastic way of telling Watson he could read him like a book.

3. "The Adventure of the Dying Detective." A bit of Holmes's improvised ravings.

4. "Silver Blaze."

5. "The Disappearance of Lady Frances Carfax." Not much of a clue here, unless you knew in which case Holmes sent Watson out of the country, but these little flights of humor are so rare in Holmes they ought to be remembered.

6. "The Adventure of the Sussex Vampire."

7. "The Adventure of the Retired Colourman." The only recorded instance of another private detective muscling in on Holmes's territory. From Watson's account of it, Mr. Barker did not seem to do such a bad job.

8. "The Adventure of the Abbey Grange." The second most famous Holmes statement. And this one he actually made.

9. "The Adventure of the Three Garridebs." A momentary glimpse at the true depth of Holmes's heart and his love for Watson.

10. "The Adventure of the Bruce-Partington Plans." In another place, Holmes describes his job as "art for art's sake," a popular philosophy of the aesthetic movement in England at the turn of the cen-

tury. We mustn't forget, however, that Holmes also had a set fee for his services; he was not independently wealthy.

11. "The Adventure of the Veiled Lodger." Another rare glimpse—this time into Holmes's sense of the spiritual. He has just finished saying to the unfortunate Mrs. Ronder, "If there is not some compensation hereafter, then the world is a cruel jest."

12. "The Final Problem." The accursed Moriarty.

13. "The Adventure of the Copper Beeches." Indeed, I would say the strangest and often most gruesome cases in the Canon take place in the countryside.

14. "His Last Bow." Holmes's poetic prophesy of a new age to come, at the end of the impending holocaust.

15. "The 'Gloria Scott.'" Chronologically, this is the first recorded deduction Holmes ever made.

16. A *Study in Scarlet*. Another first—the first words Watson ever heard Holmes utter.

17. *The Sign of Four*. Watson declines.

18. "The Adventure of the Empty House." One of the more dramatic moments in the Canon, though rather heartless on Holmes's part. Watson deserved better than this petty masquerade.

19. "His Last Bow." Holmes trained for his espionage in America, and he caught on to the lingo mighty fine.

20. "The Adventure of the Lion's Mane."

Points: 20

Your Score: _____

ANSWERS to SUPERLATIVES

1. "The 'Gloria Scott'" is Holmes's first adventure. For those of you tricked by this one into naming *A Study in Scarlet*, beware! Holmes's pre-Watson career will be coming by again.

2. "His Last Bow." Despite all the others he took part

in after his "retirement," this remains the un-
disputed final recorded case—though naturally we
are still awaiting more.

3. The Doubleday edition of *The Complete Sherlock
   Holmes* has *The Hound of the Baskervilles* running in a dead heat with *The Valley of Fear*, page-
   for-page. However, upon closer examination,
   measurement and count, I find *The Hound* is
   slightly longer than *The Valley*. (Strangely
   enough, *A Study in Scarlet* and *The Sign of Four*
   are also of very similar length at 71 and 69 pages
   respectively, though considerably shorter than the
   even 100 each for *Hound* and *Valley*.)

4. "The Naval Treaty" is the longest story in the
   Canon (among the "short" stories). It is 22 pages
   in the Doubleday edition.

5. At 7 pages, "The Adventure of the Veiled Lodger"
   is the shortest. All others listed in (4) and (5) are the
   standard 10-15 pages.

6. The longest title (38 letters) is "The Adventure of
   Charles Augustus Milverton."

7. The shortest is "His Last Bow" with 10 letters.

8. The "highest" in the Canon is "The Final Problem," set in the Swiss Alps.

9. The "lowest" story must be "The Adventure of the
   Lion's Mane," since a portion of it takes place at
   sea level. It is doubtful whether Holmes's subway
   ride in "The Red-headed League" took him below
   that level. To the best of my ability to discover,
   there are no submarine tales, the Bruce-Partington
   Plans notwithstanding. The supposed death by
   drowning of Captain Calhoun and his band remains an official mystery.

10. For "grand," I must opt for "The Adventure of the
    Illustrious Client." Practically everyone in the
    story is titled, including the bad guy, and Holmes's
    temporary employer for the case was almost un-
    doubtedly the current monarch of the Empire,
    King Edward VII. I had thought to include a
    question about the "meanest" of the tales, but so

many take place in waterfront dives, back streets and opium dens, as well as a host of other unsavory places, it would have been impossible to choose.

Points: 10

Your Score: _____

ANSWERS to MIDWAY

1-3. "A Scandal in Bohemia," "The Adventure of the Engineer's Thumb," "The Yellow Face," "The Adventure of the Wisteria Lodge," "The Greek Interpreter," and "The Disappearance of Lady Frances Carfax." Six out of sixty ain't bad.

4-7. "The Adventure of the Noble Bachelor," "The Noble Face," "The Adventure of the Missing Three-Quarter," "The Adventure of the Blanched Soldier," "The Adventure of the Creeping Man," "The Adventure of the Lion's Mane," and "The Adventure of the Shoscombe Old Place."

8-10. From "The Musgrave Ritual": Cigars in the coal-scuttle, tobacco in the toe of a Persian slipper, and correspondence affixed to the mantelpiece with a knife.

11. A gold watch. When Holmes gets hold of it in *The Sign of Four*, he is able to tell half the life history of Watson's dissolute brother.

12. On Montague Street, near the British Museum. He's there when Reginald Musgrave comes by for help.

13. *A Study in Scarlet.*

14. Seventeen. Holmes makes a point of showing up Watson's lack of observation in "A Scandal in Bohemia" with this little fact. For a man who claimed he didn't want useless knowledge—such as the fact that the earth travels around the sun—

cluttering up his mind, Holmes's interest in the number of steps to his room seems quite out of character. Perhaps he just counted them that day to try Watson.

15. An operatic contralto, a female voice of the lowest range. To imagine the dusky tones of that fiery-eyed schemer is to know real heartache. Speculation concerning the Holmes-Adler relationship is rampant and largely wishful thinking, yet one can not help but hope that on some foggy, languid afternoon Ms. Adler trod those seventeen steps and stormed Holmes's physical bastion as she had his intelligence, and with similar result.

16. Again, "A Scandal in Bohemia," plus "The Adventure of the Noble Bachelor," and "The Adventure of the Solitary Cyclist" (a near-miss).

17. A loaded hunting crop (*see* "The Six Napoleons").

18. The Diogenes Club, where, for all we know, Mycroft may still be found daily between 4:45 and 7:40.

19. In the sixth Napoleon.

20. "A Case of Identity," "The Adventure of the Dying Detective," and "The Adventure of the Mazarin Stone."

Points: 40

Your Score: _____

ANSWERS to NEWS BITS

1. "The Adventure of the Second Stain."
2. "The Adventure of the Red Circle."
3. "The Adventure of the Blue Carbuncle."
4. *The Hound of the Baskervilles.*
5. "The Adventure of the Golden Pince-Nez."
6. "The Red-headed League."

7. "The Adventure of the Cardboard Box."
8. "The Adventure of the Noble Bachelor."
9. "The Stock-broker's Clerk."
10. "The Naval Treaty."

Points: 10

Your Score: _____

ANSWERS to UNI-CLUE

1. Baritsu is that useful Japanese fighting technique Holmes said he used on Moriarty during their fight. The word is mentioned in "The Adventure of the Empty House." A thorough study of the Japanese martial arts has yet to turn up a satisfactory explanation of this technique, and I would conclude the word itself was an example of a lapse either of Watson's pen or of Holmes's tongue.

2. Leprosy rears its ugly head in "The Adventure of the Blanched Soldier." In that story, it was feared Godfrey Emsworth had contracted it during an African campaign and, because of this possibility, was being kept under wraps by the family. Holmes demonstrated otherwise and brought young Godfrey back to the light of day.

3. This was the substance with which Stapleton painted his underfed and overgrown hound in *The Hound of the Baskervilles*. Even Holmes's blood ran cold there for a few moments.

4. Holmes was an accomplished composer and musician, and one of his little hobbies was the study of historical forms of music. He wrote a monograph on the Polyphonic Motets of Lassus, an accomplishment mentioned in "The Adventure of the Bruce-Partington Plans," which was said to

102

be the "last word upon the subject." Lassus, or rather Orlando de Lassus (1532–94) was one of the late practitioners of the form, in its sacred days. A motet was a song, often unaccompanied, for a number of contrapuntal voices.

5. Credit here if you mentioned the participation of a Pinkerton agent in either *The Valley of Fear* or "The Adventure of the Red Circle," though in the latter the character was very incidental. The principal person in the former, however, was such an agent—Birdie Edwards, a.k.a. John Douglas.

6. Back to "The Bruce-Partington Plans," which were, after all, for a submarine.

7. The principal mention of bees is in "His Last Bow." There, Holmes mentions the *magnum opus* of his later years—a *Practical Handbook of Bee Culture, with some Observations upon the Segregation of the Queen*. Bees were Holmes's hobby after retirement to the Sussex Downs. Give yourself credit also if you identified the reference with "The Adventure of the Second Stain," where bees are also mentioned.

8. £6,000 was the highest stated price Holmes ever received for his services, in "The Adventure of the Priory School." At the rate of exchange at that time ($5.00 per pound), the fee is enormous, and there is some indication the Duke of Holderness actually paid Holmes twice that, though it is unlikely. Where Holmes had such difficulty early on in his career that he had to take a "roommate" to pay the rent, he now could take this single fee and buy half of Baker Street.

9. There is only one story in the Canon where the main character is an old circus performer; "The Adventure of the Veiled Lodger." Much of the background of the story takes place in the circus.

10. In "The Musgrave Ritual," Watson mentions many of Holmes's strange ways. One of these has to do with the pistol which Holmes would take up now and again and use to shoot the letters V.R. in

the wall at Baker Street. The letters, of course, stand for that gracious lady, Victoria Regina.

Points: 20

Your Score: _____

ANSWERS to ENTER TROUBLE

1. Mr. Alexander Holder's world fell down around him one night in "The Adventure of the Beryl Coronet." If it weren't for Holmes's assistance, he would have lost both a son and a reputation. As it was, he lost a pretty unsavory niece: "Women are never to be trusted. . . ."
2. "The Resident Patient." Holmes's operation was successful, but the patient died.
3. I love it! Dr. Grimesby Roylott in "The Adventure of the Speckled Band."
4. "The Adventure of the Missing Three-Quarter." For once, even Holmes was stumped by this garble. But when the air was cleared , he granted amateur sport to be "the best and soundest thing in England."
5. "The Adventure of the Black Peter." I've always thought with a little paint on his face Holmes would be a dead ringer for Queequeg.
6. "The Adventure of the Engineer's Thumb." Mr. Victor Hatherley is possessed of what has to be the strongest constitution and evenest humor of anyone in the Canon. He has lost a thumb only a few hours earlier, and seems quite able now to enter upon a very long discussion of the whole matter, never once exhibiting the excruciating pain he must be under. Had Dr. Watson filled him with morphine, he never would be able to present so lucid an account of his adventures.

7. "A Scandal in Bohemia." First in a long line of pompous nobility.

8. "The Musgrave Ritual." From the structure of the quotation, you can assume it is a tale Holmes is informing Watson of, and indeed, it is a tale from Holmes's pre-Watsonian days—a tale so good one can say the only thing it lacks is the presence of the good doctor himself.

9. "The Adventure of the Noble Bachelor." This ass doesn't get the girl either—just as the bloody King of Bohemia lost out.

10. "The Adventure of the Charles Augustus Milverton." The girl gets *him*.

11. "The Adventure of the Norwood Builder." No one excels Inspector Lestrade in running down the wrong man.

12. *The Sign of Four*. Watson's darling, Mary, and an enviable postal system.

13. *The Hound of the Baskervilles*.

14. "The Adventure of the Priory School." Poor Dr. Huxtable is one up on Alexander Holder.

15. "A Case of Identity." One of the finest visual moments in the Canon.

Points: 15

Your Score: _____

ANSWERS to CRYPTO-QUIZ

1. The letters ETAO etc. are the most often-used letters in English. "E" is used most often, "T" second most often, "A" third, etc. This knowledge aided Holmes in deciphering the messages in "The Adventure of the Dancing Men."

2. "Gone," "come," "sun," and "shadow" from the glorious "Musgrave Ritual."

3. "The Adventure of the Red Circle" and "the Greek Interpreter," respectively.

4. *The Valley of Fear*. The numbers are references to a

particular page and column of a book and to the words in the column which, put together, formed the message.

5. Read every third word, starting with the first, and you'll have not only the answer but the story as well. It's a fairly silly construction, I know, but it certainly makes as much sense as Beddoes's message to Old Trevor.

Points: 10

Your Score: _____

ANSWERS to PICK A MURDER

1. Peter himself in "The Adventure of the Black Peter." Peter Carey, for the sticklers.
2. Brunton from "The Musgrave Ritual."
3. Arthur Pimmer, in "The Adventure of the Stockbroker's Clerk." For once, an unsuccessful attempt. One wishes Holmes had given him a little more time.
4. Lady Frances from "The Disappearance of Lady Frances Carfax." Again, unsuccessul—but grotesque! This is also one of the most unwieldy tales in the Canon. Why the Reverend Dr. Shlessinger (Holy Peters) didn't nick the old lady's jugular and depart for the nearest steamer instead of going through this involved business is a bigger mystery than everything which proceeds it.
5. Ted Baldwin, *The Valley of Fear*. Everyone thought it was good guy John Douglas for most of the story. It's understandable, since the ghastly wound would lend the dead man's features a certain air of anonymity.
6. "The Greek Intepreter." The poor unfortunate, surely one of the most pathetic creatures in the Canon, was Paul Kratides.

7. Mr. Hatherley, who gets out with his life, but loses a thumb in "The Adventure of the Engineer's Thumb."

8. Bartholomew Sholto, at the receiving end of Tonga's blow gun in *The Sign of Four*.

9. In "The Adventure of the Retired Colourman," Josiah Amberly chose this means of ridding himself of his unfaithful wife (who wouldn't be?) and her paramour, Dr. Ray Ernest.

10. Fitzroy MacPherson in "The Adventure of the Lion's Mane."

11. Mortimer Tregennis, from "The Adventure of the Devil's Foot."

12. Julie Stoner in "The Adventure of the Speckled Band."

13. Selden and the two Sir Baskervilles, Charles and Henry, are victims of the hound in *The Hound of the Baskervilles*, though Henry lives.

14. The Honourable Ronald Adair is killed in "The Adventure of the Empty House." Holmes's dummy took one in the head.

15. Mr. Straker in "Silver Blaze." Better than a split-level coffin.

Points: 30

Your Score: _____

ANSWERS to THE MASTER ACTS

1. By laying down a fine cover of cigarette ash, Holmes sees it has been walked upon by someone other than Professor Coram. "The Adventure of the Golden Pince-Nez." (Give yourself credit as well if you mentioned instead either the business of food consumption or the interesting coincidence of lost glasses and identical floor covering.)

2. In "A Case of Identity," the most telling evidence is

the typewriter—Holmes knew Hosmer's letters were written in Windibank's office.

3. Holmes deduced that the chipped rock on Thor Bridge revealed the method Mrs. Gibson used to get rid of the gun. "The Adventure of the Thor Bridge."

4. The level to which the parsley had sunk in the butter. "The Adventure of the Six Napoleons."

5. The horse that drove the carriage which picked up Hatherley at the station was fresh. The long drive to the house, therefore, was a blind. This is the only deduction Holmes makes in "The Adventure of the Engineer's Thumb," and generally he comes out looking downright ineffectual throughout the story."

6. In "The 'Gloria Scott,'" Holmes spots the tattoo Old Trevor had vainly attempted to eradicate.

7. Holmes reads Watson's mind by following the good doctor's expressions while Watson reads the paper, observes two portraits on the wall, and finally touches his old wound. "The Resident Patient."

8. In "The Adventure of the Three Students," Holmes's clues were Bannister's planting himself in the chair, Gilchrist's height, and the evidence of track shoes in the study. It's one of the better tales for mystery "purists."

9. An advertisement supposedly written in England by an Englishman contained several American expressions and words, "The Adventure of the Three Garridebs."

10. There is no bloodstain on the floor under the stain on the rug; therefore the rug had been removed and replaced for some reason. From "The Adventure of the Second Stain," of course.

Points: 20

Your Score: _____

1-4. Silver Blaze in the story of that name, and Shoscombe Prince in "The Adventure of Shoscombe Old Place."

5-8. Toby in *The Sign of Four* and Pompey in "The Adventure of the Missing Three-Quarter."

9-12. The snake in "The Adventure of the Speckled Band" and the hound in *The Hound of the Baskervilles*.

13-14. *Cyanea capillata* in "The Adventure of the Lion's Mane."

15. Inside a goose.

16. Professor Moriarty in "The Final Problem."

17. "As I watched him I was irresistibly reminded of a pure-blooded, well-trained foxhound, as it dashes back and forward through the covert, whining in its eagerness, until it comes across the lost scent.

18. Mrs. Hudson's ailing dog was the subject of the test. The dog died. Mrs. Hudson is never mentioned by name, by the way, until the second case, *The Sign of Four*. Holmes seems to call the landlady "Mrs. Turner" in "A Scandal in Bohemia," though it is unclear. Mrs. Turner could have been a servant of Mrs. Hudson's.

19. He was injected with monkey hormones—and the results couldn't have been funnier if he'd squatted down, scratched his ribs, and grunted for a banana.

20. The circus lion attacked her and tore away a significant portion of her face.

Points: 20

Your Score: _____

1. Reginald Musgrave—"The Musgrave Ritual."
2. Grant Munro—"The Yellow Face."
3. Mr. Melas—"The Greek Interpreter."
4. Dr. Grimesby Roylott—"The Adventure of the Speckled Band."
5. Watson—*The Sign of Four.*
6. James Ryder—"The Adventure of the Blue Carbuncle."
7. Neville St. Clair—"The Man with the Twisted Lip."
8. Professor Moriarty—"The Final Problem."
9. Watson—"Silver Blaze."
10. Holmes—"The Reigate Puzzle."
11. Victor Hatherley—"The Adventure of the Engineer's Thumb."
12. Stamford—*A Study in Scarlet.*
13. Mary Sutherland—"A Case of Identity."
14. Percy Phelps—"The Naval Treaty.
15. Hall Pycroft—"The Adventure of the Stockbroker's Clerk."
16. Jabez Wilson—"The Red-headed League."
17. Watson—"The Five Orange Pips."
18. Alexander Holder—"The Adventure of the Beryl Coronet."
19. Old Trevor—"The 'Gloria Scott.'"
20. Irene Adler—"A Scandal in Bohemia."
21. Violet Hunter—"The Adventure of the Copper Beeches."
22. Hattie Doran Moulton—"The Adventure of the Noble Bachelor."
23. Nancy Barclay—"The Adventure of the Crooked Man."
24. James McCarthy—"The Boscombe Valley Mystery."
25. Dr. Percy Trevelyan—"The Resident Patient."

Points: 50

Your Score: _____

Part I

1. Christmas.
2. "It was in the Spring of the year 1894 . . ."
3. Because more than one person takes a dip in the ocean—never an unmixed joy in England, and positively deadly in the colder months (though I suppose you can always find some wonderful old eccentric taking his daily "bathe" year-round at the age of 86).
4. The river under the bridge would almost certainly have been frozen, and Mrs. Gibson's plan would have been even more short-lived than it was.

5-8. Nine o'clock at night, August 2nd, 1914.

Part II

The order as follows:
1. "The 'Gloria Scott'"—Holmes's first case.
2. "The Musgrave Ritual"—his second recorded case.
3. *A Study in Scarlet*. The first case after meeting Watson.
4. *The Valley of Fear*. Moriarty is still alive (pre-1891), and Watson is unmarried and still living with Holmes.
5. "The Boscombe Valley Mystery." Mary appears here as Watson's wife (she goes out of his life sometime during Holmes's absence and believed death).
6. "The Final Problem"—wherein Moriarty dies and Holmes disappears, only to return in
7. "The Adventure of the Empty House."
8. And finally, "The Adventure of the Lion's Mane," which takes place during Holmes's retirement and is set near his home in Sussex.

Points: 16

Your Score: _____

ANSWERS to WEAPONS

1F.   Remember her neat trick with the bridge?

2C.   *The Valley of Fear.*

3A.   Holmes's dummy was also the air-gun's victim.

4G.   Just deserts. "The Adventure of the Red Circle."

5N.   The innocent bystander in "The Adventure of the Golden Pince-Nez."

6D.   The only indoor lynching I've ever come across. "The Resident Patient."

7J.   "The Adventure of the Veiled Lodger," who was rather worse off than her husband.

8I.   A fitting fall for a man who'd risen so high in crime.

9B.   "The Adventure of the Retired Colourman."

10E.   Presumed drowned with his cohorts in "The Five Orange Pips."

11M.   *The Sign of Four.*

12L.   The hound, of course.

13O.   Perhaps the most horrible way to go in all the Canon.

14K.   "The Adventure of the Dying Detective."

15H.   "The Greek Interpreter." For an overall miserable experience, Kratides wins hands down.

Points: 15

Your Score: _____

ANSWERS to FOREIGN SHORES

1. Effie Munro in "The Yellow Face." The love her husband eventually showed makes up for Holmes's misreading of the entire situation.
2. Old Trevor in "The 'Gloria Scott.'" His misplaced charity that day finally killed him.
3. Jefferson Hope—*A Study in Scarlet*
4. Hattie Doran Moulton in "The Adventure of the Noble Bachelor."
5. Abe Slaney in "The Adventure of the Dancing Men."
6. Mrs. Gibson in "The Problem of Thor Bridge."
7. The King of Bohemia in "A Scandal in Bohemia." If the surmise is correct, it wouldn't be the only time Holmes served the King of England.
8. Don Murillo in "The Adventure of Wisteria Lodge."
9. Captain James Calhoun again in "The Five Orange Pips." One murderer in the Canon, by the way, whom we never see.
10. Black Gorgiano in "The Adventure of the Red Circle."
11. Charles McCarthy in "The Boscombe Valley Mystery."
12. John Douglas, a.k.a. "Birdie" Edwards, a.k.a. John McMurdo. *The Valley of Fear.*
13. Professor Coram in "The Adventure of the Golden Pince-Nez."
14. Jonathan Small in *The Sign of Four.*
15. "The Disappearance of Lady Frances Carfax," in which we encounter Holmes in Montpellier, France.

Points: 30

Your Score: _____

113

1. Only three.

2-3. "The Greek Interpreter," "The Final Problem," and "The Adventure of the Bruce-Partington Plans."

4. None! In *The Valley of Fear,* Inspector Mac-Donald only *reports* having talked with Moriarty. And in "The Final Problem" he is reported as being at the Reichenbach Falls in Holmes's note to Watson. But he is never seen by Watson nor by the reader except through hearsay from other people. Unbelievable, but true.

5-6. "The Adventure of the Blanched Soldier" and "The Adventure of the Lion's Mane." Both are fairly unremarkable.

7-8. "The Adventure of the Mazarin Stone" and "His Last Bow." The former is decidedly second-rate and the latter is sublime.

9. They were all accused of crimes they did not commit. Holmes got them all off the hook. If the great detective couldn't always collar the bad guy, his ability to clear the innocent was unerring.

10. They were all involved in cases mentioned by Watson but never chronicled.

11. French (*A Study in Scarlet*); German (*The Sign of Four*); Latin ("The Red-headed League"); Italian ("The Adventure of the Red Circle"); and, of course, English.

12-13. "The Adventure of Charles Augustus Milverton"; "The Adventure of the Bruce-Partington Plans"; and "The Adventure of the Illustrious Client." The Copper Beeches episode does not qualify — no felony was intended, and the act was performed with the aid and consent of a member of the household.

14. By the murder of the Honourable Richard Adair. The first sentence in "The Adventure of the Empty House" has always appealed to me as a

fine example of Watson's elegant but straight-forward prose.

15. Somewhere in the vaults of Cox & Co., at Charing Cross. It contains all Watson's notes on unchronicled cases, and its discovery is avidly awaited, but with dwindling hope.

16. The world's only unofficial consulting detective. He also said he was the last and highest court of appeal in detection. Pretty impressive for a fellow who couldn't go it alone on the rent. But he doubtless foresaw his own bright future.

17. A 7 per-cent solution, three times a day for several months.

18. They were all men guilty of felonies whom Holmes allowed to go free. They are by no means the only guilty parties in the Canon Holmes let off on his own authority.

19. "The Man with the Twisted Lip."

20. Just a touch of rheumatism.

Points: 40

Your Score: _____

ANSWERS to A RELATIONSHIP

1. Watson is speaking of Holmes's sincere (and emotionally overwrought) concern for him after he was wounded in "The Adventure of the Three Garridebs."

2-3. According to Watson in "The Adventure of the Veiled Lodger," he aided Holmes for 17 of the detective's 23 years of active practice. D. Martin Dakin, in *A Sherlock Holmes Commentary*, feels this shorts Watson by two years, an astute observation with which I agree. Mr. Dakin suggests a typesetter's slip, changing a 9 to a 7. This would seem the most logical conclusion. (Answer correct within 2)

4. "The Adventure of the Devil's Foot," in which Watson saves them both from a very successful experiment.

5. Watson is living with Holmes at the beginning of 38 tales. The other 22 include those during his marriage, after Holmes's retirement, while the doctor was temporarily away, and, of course, *A Study in Scarlet*. (Answer correct within 2)

6. He supplied a distant relation of his with the money to buy out Watson's practice. Watson finally caught on—several years later.

7. Murder. Had "Killer" Evans' bullet proved fatal, he would have died at Holmes's hands.

8. They all took on Watson's practice so he could be with Holmes on his cases—Jackson and Anstruther as a temporary favor, Verner as a permanent replacement. He was the distant relation from Question 6.

9. Never.

10. They are talking quietly on the terrace of a great gabled house, perched on a chalk cliff, overlooking the sea in the dead of night at the dawn of World War I.

Points: 10

Your Score: _____

1. Fifty-five shillings from a "Jew broker" in Tottenham Court Road. Martin Dakin (p. 223) takes exception to Holmes's bragging about picking up the 500-guinea Stradivarius for a song. I take exception, however, to Holmes's racist insinuations about the Jews. From "The Adventure of the Cardboard Box."

2. Mathews, in the waiting room of Charing Cross. Another case mentioned but unchronicled, from Holmes's famous "M" file in "The Adventure of the Empty House."

3. 1. Italy (Florence); 2. Tibet; 3. Persia (or Iran); 4. Saudi Arabia (Mecca); 5. The Sudan (Khartoum); and 6. France (Montpellier).

4. He had discovered a "re-agent which is precipitated by haemoglobin, and by nothing else." Subsequent scientific commentators have had some difficulty explaining either the process or the real importance of this discovery. It is never mentioned by Holmes again.

5. They are the owners, respectively of Toby and Pompey, the two hounds Holmes uses for tracing in *The Sign of Four* and "The Adventure of the Missing Three-Quarter."

6. "A Scandal in Bohemia" and "The Adventure of the Norwood Builder."

7. Colonel James Moriarty, strangely enough. The professor apparently had a second brother, unnamed, though conceivably another James, who works as a stationmaster. This plethora of Moriartys led John Gardner into a paroxym of foolish speculation in his recent novel, *The Return of Moriarty*.

8. Holmes's pseudonym during The Great Hiatus. His exploits were apparently reported on in the news between 1891 and 1894.

9. Charing Cross Hospital. The initials on a cane left at 221B by Dr. Mortimer in *The Hound of the Baskervilles* led Holmes and Watson into a debate about the owner. Part of the debate concerned these initials inscribed on a silver band around the cane. Holmes won, of course.

10. This was the terrorist body in Vermissa Valley which Birdie Edwards joined as a spy for the Pinkertons in *The Valley of Fear*.

11. To explain the torn bird, a pail of blood and the charred bones in "The Adventure of the Wisteria Lodge."

12. A full counterfeiter's outfit: press, plates and paper.

13. Stanley Hopkins, the young police inspector, who first appears in "The Adventure of the Black Peter."

14. They are the owners of the Six Napoleons (Dr. Barnicot owned two of them.)

15. "The Adventure of the Abbey Grange," where Lady Brakenstall's story collapses under Holmes's all-seeing eye.

16. They all came to 221B to warn Holmes off cases and to threaten him.

17. Billy is a page in Holmes's employ who appears in a few of the later tales and, strangely enough, in the pre-1891 *Valley of Fear*. Dakin (p.264) proposes the likelihood of two Billy's in Holmes's history, accounting for this earlier one.

18. "The Adventure of the Sussex Vampire." Commentators will be speculating for more years than they already have about this reference to a formal organization. It is really more likely that Holmes was speaking tongue-in-cheek than he actually had set up an agency. One thinks of the stodgy note from the firm of Morrison, Morrison, and Dodd which opens the case and one imagines Holmes temporarily adopting somewhat of a corporate vocabulary as an ironic comment on that document.

19. Holmes has a telephone at 221B in these stories.

20. That's right—never. They are "Holmes" and "Watson" to the end. Doubtless one day in some heavenly Baker Street, as Holmes divines yet another treasured secret from the depths of his friend's heart, Watson will ruffle up his flawless wings and once again exclaim, "My dear Holmes! How on earth did you know that!" And Holmes, picking a bit of lint off his more tarnished set, will grin his mischievous grin, and say, finally, "Elementary, my dear Watson."

Points: 60

Your Score: _____

ANSWERS to ROGUES' GALLERY

1. 1. "The Adventure of the Engineer's Thumb."
   2. Lysander Stark.
   3. Victor Hatherley.
   4. Hatherley describes the drop from the sill as being about 30 feet. If the distance between his left hand and his feet is about 6-7 feet, he is about to drop 23 feet.
   5. She is the woman inside the house who helps Hatherley make his escape.

2. 1. *A Study in Scarlet.*
   2. Inspector G. Lestrade of Scotland Yard.
   3. He thinks it is part of the name "Rachel," but it really means "revenge," in German.
   4. Number 3, Lauriston Gardens.
   5. They meet for the first time.

3. 1. "The Crooked Man."
   2. A mongoose.
   3. Nancy Devoe Barclay.
   4. Nancy's husband.
   5. Apoplexy, apparently caused by a sudden reminder of a shameful past.

4. 1. The King of Bohemia.
2. He is described by Watson as being not less than six feet six inches.
3. Count Von Kramm is the pseudonym he tries out on Holmes, with no success.
4. £1,000.
5. "A Scandal in Bohemia."

5. 1. She was hired as a governess, officially, though her boss had other uses for her.
2. Her hair has been cut in a distinctly non-Victorian style.
3. Blue (rather a large point is made of her being forced to assume a certain identity).
4. He is attacked by a hungry mastiff.
5. "The Adventure of the Copper Beeches."

6. 1. "The Reigate Puzzle."
2. Holmes and Watson.
3. They are articles stolen from a neighboring house in the story. The robbery was a "phony" and Holmes spotted it as such, owing to the arbitrary and fairly unvaluable items stolen.
4. William the coachman.
5. Alec and old man Cunningham.

7. 1. "The Adventure of the Solitary Cyclist."
2. Woodley.
3. Something of a "kangaroo wedding," being presided over by a defrocked priest.
4. Unknown to her, she is heir of a rather large fortune.
5. He is sent out by Holmes to investigate the situation on his own.

8. 1. They are in the home of Eduardo Lucas.
2. A top-secret communication from a foreign leader which has disappeared.
3. He knew the rug had been moved after a murder had been committed because the floor and the bloodstains didn't match. That is, of course, "The Adventure of the Second Stain."

4. He was murdered by his French wife.

5. Mrs. Trelawney Hope.

9. 1. The "bride" has dropped her bouquet and the man in the pew picked it up, and is now handing it back.

2. Lord St. Simon, Hattie Doran, Francis Hay Moulton.

3. "The Adventure of the Noble Bachelor."

4. No one.

5. Because Hattie was already married to Moulton, she could not legally be Mrs. (or Lady) St. Simon.

10. 1. "The Musgrave Ritual."

2. The butler.

3. Rachel Howells closed the door on him and later disappeared without a trace.

4. Watson is of no help to Holmes in this story. Though, unfortunately, he rarely is, in this case he has a good excuse. They hadn't met yet.

5. The jewels belonged to the Stuart family, which reigned in England from 1603 to 1714, with a short vacation during the Commonwealth.

11. 1. Mr. Neville St. Clair.

2. Isa Whitney's wife comes to Watson's wife, asking her to help her bring home her husband from his opium den. Watson went there—.

3. In the opium den, in search of Isa Whitney, and runs into Holmes in the middle of a case.

4. Boone is the pseudonym St. Clair uses during his jaunts at begging.

5. "James," believed to be a pet name of Mrs. Watson for her husband, as she is the only one who ever calls him that.

12. 1. Jim Browner.

2. To S. Cushing. Thanks to the initial instead of the first name, it will reach the wrong party.

3. He sends it to revenge himself upon the woman who ruined his marriage.

4. The portraits of Henry Ward Beecher and General Gordon.

    5. Edgar Allen Poe.

13. 1. "The Adventure of the Abbey Grange."
    2. Beeswing is another name for the dregs in a wine bottle. It is the question of those dregs which first puts Holmes onto the scent.
    3. "The game is afoot."
    4. Captain Crocker.
    5. Theresa.

14. 1. "The Final Problem"
    2. The Reichenbach Falls in the Swiss Alps.
    3. 1891.
    4. On his way back to the lodge to tend to a non-existent patient.
    5. Colonel Sebastian Moran.

Points: 70

Your Score: _____

— CORRIGENDUM —

Due to a really silly printer's error, there is a mistake on page 123 of this book. The word "Rules" at the top of the page should have been omitted since "The Rules of the Game" actually are on page iii. Please excuse any awkwardness this may create and just enjoy the book!

RULES

"How often have I said to you that when you have eliminated the impossible, whatever remains, however improbable, must be the truth?"

Sherlock Holmes

ILLUSTRATION ACKNOWLEDGEMENTS

1. Sidney Paget (the greatest of the English illustrators—he first put Holmes in the deerstalker cap). The *Strand Magazine*, March, 1892.
2. George Hutchinson, 1891.
3. Sidney Paget, July, 1893. (All Paget illustrations are from the *Strand Magazine*.)
4. Sidney Paget, July, 1891.
5. Sidney Paget, June, 1892.
6. Sidney Paget, June, 1893.
7. Sidney Paget, January, 1904.
8. Sidney Paget, December, 1904.
9. Sidney Paget, April, 1892.
10. Sidney Paget, May, 1893.
11. Sidney Paget, December, 1891.
12. Sidney Paget, January, 1893.
13. Frederic Dorr Steele for *Collier's Magazine*, December 31, 1904. Steele is the greatest of the American illustrators, and first pictured Holmes with his curved pipe.
14. Sidney Paget, December, 1893. The picture which gave visual reality to the grief that struck England and the world in 1891 at Reichenbach Falls.

SOURCES OF CHAPTER EPIGRAMS

All those quotations given as epigrams of each section are, of course, taken from the Canon. Here is each title again, with the story from which its quotation is taken.

For Openers:	*A Study in Scarlet*
Titles:	"The Problem of Thor Bridge"
Partners in Crime:	"The Musgrave Ritual"
A.K.A.:	"The Adventure of the Three Garridebs"
Our Master's Voice I:	*The Sign of Four*
Memorable Villains:	"The Adventure of Charles Augustus Milverton"
Open And Shut:	"The Adventure of the Priory School"
On Stage:	*The Sign of Four*
Dainty Things:	*The Sign of Four*
Our Master's Voice II:	?
Superlatives:	"The Adventure of the Devil's Foot"
Midway:	*A Study in Scarlet*
News Bits:	*The Hound of the Baskervilles*
Uni-Clue:	"The Yellow Face"
Enter Trouble:	*The Hound of the Baskervilles*
Crypto-Quiz:	"The 'Gloria Scott'"
Pick A Murder:	*A Study in Scarlet*
The Master Acts:	*A Study in Scarlet*
Animal Kingdom:	"The Adventure of the Sussex Vampire"

Quotables:	"A Scandal in Bohemia"
An Elementary Chronology:	"The Adventure of the Second Stain"
Weapons:	"The Adventure of Charles Augustus Milverton"
Foreign Shores:	*The Sign of Four*
The Home Stretch:	"The Final Problem"
A Relationship	"The Adventure of the Three Garridebs"
Super-Impossibles:	*The Sign of Four*

SCORECARD

On the facing page are all the quiz sections with their maximum possible scores. Compare your scores, add them up, and find your rating at the bottom of the page.

RATE YOURSELF

625 +: Congratulations! You have won The Sherlock Holmes Grand Master Award of Awards.

575-624: Excellent! The Stanley Hopkins Promising Young Detective Commendation.

450-574: Not bad, really. The John H. Watson Meritorious If Unenlightened Companion Award.

0-449: You definitely need more reading and study. You have won the G. Lestrade Booby Prize.

Title	Possible Score	Your Score
FOR OPENERS	20	
TITLES	30	
PARTNERS IN CRIME	20	
A.K.A.	20	
OUR MASTER'S VOICE I	20	
MEMORABLE VILLAINS	30	
OPEN AND SHUT	20	
ON STAGE	10	
DAINTY THINGS	30	
OUR MASTER'S VOICE II	20	
SUPERLATIVES	10	
MIDWAY	40	
NEWS BITS	10	
UNI-CLUE	20	
ENTER TROUBLE	15	
CRYPTO-QUIZ	10	
PICK A MURDER	30	
THE MASTER ACTS	20	
ANIMAL KINGDOM	20	
QUOTABLES	50	
AN ELEMENTARY CHRONOLOGY	16	
WEAPONS	15	
FOREIGN SHORES	30	
THE HOME STRETCH	40	
A RELATIONSHIP	10	
SUPER-IMPOSSIBLES	60	
ROGUES' GALLERY	70	
Total:	686